BASIC ELECTRONICS

BASIC ELECTRONICS

by **ALFRED A. LEASE, Ph.D.**

**Professor and Chairman, Department of
Industrial Engineering and Technology
St. Cloud State College, St. Cloud, Minnesota**

THE BRUCE PUBLISHING COMPANY

Milwaukee

Library of Congress Catalog Card Number: 65–28208

Copyright © 1965 THE BRUCE PUBLISHING COMPANY
MADE IN THE UNITED STATES OF AMERICA

. . . to Joan

PREFACE

This book is based upon the premise that new concepts must be presented one step at a time, with sufficient exploration of each step to insure reinforcement and total comprehension. Small concepts sequentially serve as the skeletal framework upon which are built broad generalizations and principles of electronics.

At the end of each unit the student will find problems which have been carefully constructed to summarize the material presented, provoke thought, and encourage the cultivation of meaningful problem-solving techniques. Answers are provided in the appendix which permit the student to determine, with minimal delay, the correctness of his responses. The answers should first be written on a separate sheet of paper, and then compared with the answers in the text.

It will be noted that this book does not contain projects or so-called "laboratory exercises." This textbook accepts the philosophy that laboratory exercises are a "must" for total comprehension, but such experiential activity cannot adequately be presented as part of a standard textbook. It is a specialized activity which must receive specialized treatment. Such laboratory experience is professionally and expertly handled by experiment kits and experiment workbooks now being used by schools throughout the nation. The Instruct-A-Kit 101, produced by the Instruct-A-Kit Company of St. Cloud, Minnesota, is one such unit.

Many basic electronics textbooks minimize arithmetical computation on the pretext that students fear arithmetic and therefore will not comprehend electronics books using a mathematical frame of reference. This textbook has been designed on the thesis that applied mathematics is the very basis of electronics, and that the subject cannot be thoroughly understood without using computational methods. It is appreciated that many students may lack the necessary background for using mathematics as a tool. In order to bridge this latter chasm, this book teaches the proper manipulation of mathematical concepts. In accomplishing this objective meaningless abstract problems have been carefully averted, and instead the examples presented are meaningful for the student because they are based upon the subject matter being learned — electronics. This latter feature prevents the frustration many persons have experienced when forced to learn about meaningless bushels of wheat, or about trains traveling across the continent at unrealistic rates of speed. The problems are practical, realistic, and most of all directly applicable.

This text has been specifically prepared for basic courses in electronics at the high school and freshman college level. It may, however, be used to very good advantage by anyone wishing to learn about this fascinating science. Because of the manner in which the subject matter has been handled, all users of this book will discover a new dimension in learning, whether or not he has the advantage of the services of a teacher in a formal classroom.

Sincere appreciation is expressed to the following companies for their permission to use pictures which are contained in this book:

Allis Chalmers Manufacturing Co., Milwaukee, Wisconsin
Burgess Battery Company, Freeport, Illinois
Delco Radio Division, General Motors Corporation, Kokomo, Indiana
Electric Machinery Manufacturing Company, Minneapolis, Minnesota
Electronic Associates, Inc., Long Branch, New Jersey
Hughes Semiconductor Division, Hughes Aircraft Corporation, Newport Beach, California
International Rectifier Corporation, El Segundo, California
International Resistance Company, Philadelphia, Pennsylvania
Motorola Semiconductor Products Incorporated, Phoenix, Arizona
Radio Corporation of America, New York, New York
Sprague Electric Company, North Adams, Massachusetts
Superior Electric Company, Bristol, Connecticut
Triplett Electrical Instrument Company, Bluffton, Ohio
U. S. Department of the Interior, Bureau of Reclamation, Washington, D. C.
Wisconsin Electric Power Co., Milwaukee, Wisconsin

CONTENTS

BASIC ELECTRONICS

Unit 1

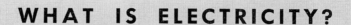

WHAT IS ELECTRICITY?

When one looks at a pencil, or a desk, or a piece of paper, it is difficult to understand what these things have in common with electricity. As a matter of fact, all things — all matter — are directly related to this marvelous force called electricity. What is this relationship? To understand this it is necessary to take a look at matter. It is necessary to "take it apart," to see "what makes it tick," and to see "how it is made."

Molecules

All matter is made of little building blocks called *molecules* (*mahl*-ee-kules). If one were to divide a drop of water again and again and again until the tiniest bit of water imaginable remained, that tiny bit of matter would be one molecule of water. Millions of molecules combine to form a drop of water. *All things* are made of these tiny building blocks. Even humans *are made of many different kinds of molecules.*

Atoms

One molecule of water can be broken down even smaller. When a molecule is broken down into smaller parts, it is no longer a molecule, but instead becomes *atoms* (*at*-ums). For example, one molecule of water contains three atoms. There are two atoms of hydrogen and one atom of oxygen in one molecule of water.

Thus one molecule of water equals:

$$H + H + O = H_2O$$

Two atoms of hydrogen plus one atom of oxygen equal one molecule of water.

What is an atom? *Atoms,* like molecules, are *building blocks,* but they are even *smaller than molecules,* and they are made of only one kind of matter called an *element* (*el-ĕ-ment*).

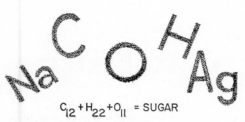

$C_{12} + H_{22} + O_{11}$ = SUGAR

Elements

There are just a few more than 100 known elements in the world. Carbon, silver, oxygen, hydrogen, sodium, chlorine are all examples of elements. Sugar is made of the elements carbon, hydrogen, and oxygen. It may seem peculiar but the basic molecules of wood are *also* made of carbon, hydrogen, and oxygen. How can this be? The reason is that wood contains *different amounts* of each of these elements than does sugar.

Protons and Electrons

If one were to examine a clock in order to determine what parts were inside, he would find wheels, springs, bolts, gears, and many other interesting things. An atom does not have bolts and gears, but it does have other things which are just as interesting. An atom is made of many parts, but the two of most interest are the *electron* (ee-*lek*-tron) and

**PROTONS
are "+"**

**ELECTRONS
are "—"**

the proton (*pro*-ton). The proton is found in the *center* of the atom while the electron revolves around the proton. The proton, which is 1845 times heavier than the tiny electron, has a positive electrical charge. The electron has a negative electrical charge.

Just as there are no two people who look alike, the atom of one element is different from the atom of another element. They differ in the number of electrons and protons contained within each atom. An atom of hydrogen will have a different number of electrons and protons than an atom of oxygen. To help distinguish between an atom of one element and the atoms of other elements, students sometimes draw diagrams of atoms.

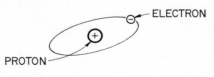

The *center* of the atom is called the *nucleus* (*new*-klee-us). You will remember protons, or matter with a plus (+) charge of electricity are found in the nucleus. Racing around the outside of the nucleus, like a missile in orbit, are the *negatively charged electrons* (−).

Hydrogen is the simplest element. It has one proton and one electron.

Helium has two electrons and two protons.

Other elements have different numbers of electrons and protons.

4

Electrical Charges

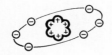 

(+)'S = (−)'S = NEUTRAL

When any atom has an equal number of electrons and protons it is said to be *neutral* (*new*-trul). Thus an atom having six protons in the center, must also have six electrons orbiting around the outside if it is to be neutral. If it has more positive charges (+) than negative charges (−), it is positively charged. On the other hand, a negatively charged atom has more electrons than protons.

If a neutral atom were to lose an electron, it would have a positive charge because there would be more protons than electrons.

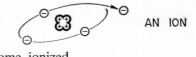

POSITIVE

NEGATIVE

If a neutral atom could lose one or more protons (which cannot actually happen), it would have a negative charge because it would then have more electrons than protons.

Atoms which have either lost or gained electrons are said to be *charged atoms* or *ions* (*eye*-ons), and they are referred to as being *ionized*. Ions are found everywhere. Even molecules become ionized.

AN ION

Free Electrons

It is a fact that atoms and molecules often lose or gain electrons. These electrons are known as *free electrons*. Matter which has a plentiful supply of free electrons is known as a (con-*duck*-tor), and you know from past experience that copper and other metals are conductors. Matter which has few or no free electrons are *insulators* (*in*-sul-ate-or), or *nonconductors,* for example, glass, rubber, and plastic.

COPPER WIRE = **CONDUCTOR**

GLASS = **INSULATOR**

Free electrons easily move about from place to place. When they do it is said they *flow* from one point to another. Electron flow is usually referred to as a flow of *current* (*cur*-rent).

5

You may recall having learned a basic rule of electricity: *Like charges repel and unlike charges attract.* Thus two positive charges repel one another. Two negative charges also repel one another, *but* a positive charge and a negative charge attract. This peculiarity of attraction and repulsion are important to the flow of electrons.

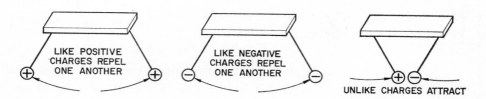

LIKE POSITIVE CHARGES REPEL ONE ANOTHER

LIKE NEGATIVE CHARGES REPEL ONE ANOTHER

UNLIKE CHARGES ATTRACT

If there is a piece of matter which has a heavy positive charge, and another piece of matter having an excess of electrons, the two charges will try to get together because unlike charges attract. How could one help them get together? By connecting a wire conductor between the two charged pieces of matter. The excess electrons would then flow over the wire conductor to the excess protons which are hungry for company. When the two forces would balance, the piece of matter would again be neutralized, and there would be as many plus charges on it as there would be minus charges.

ELECTRONS FLOW

Coulombs

The more positive or the more negative an atom is, the more *charge* it is said to have. Charge is measured in *coulombs* (*koo*-loms), which *represent a quantity of electricity.* For example, water is never measured by the number of molecules in a given quantity, but instead is measured in gallons. On the other hand, charge is never measured in the number of electrons, but instead it is measured in coulombs.

6,280,000,000,000,000,000 electrons

One coulomb of charge is equal to 6.28 billion billion electrons. This is sometimes written by scientists as 6.28×10^{18}. Instead of writing out the word "coulomb," it is abbreviated to the symbol **Q.** *Q* is an electrical charge; it represents *quantity.*

Electric *current* is *not* the same as charge, but rather is the *flow* of charge (coulombs). A coulomb is a quantity of electricity just as a gallon of water is a quantity of water. On the other hand current considers not only quantity but *rate* (speed) at which electrons flow. Of course, whenever one talks about rate or speed, he is really talking in terms of *time*. Time is abbreviated to "t" when working with formulas.

Amperes

Current refers to electron flow in a given unit of time, and it is measured in *amperes* (*am*-peers). One ampere is equivalent to 6.28 billion billion electrons passing a given point in one second. This is the same as saying one coulomb of electrons flowing past a point in one second is equal to one ampere.

THE FORMULA
1 Q/second = 1 amp.

Just as the symbol Q stands for charge (coulombs), the symbol I stands for current (amperes), and is sometimes abbreviated to "amps."

REMEMBER
Current = Amp. = I

To summarize, then, current (I), which is measured in amperes, represents the amount of electrons flowing past a point in a given amount of time. If 6,280,000,000,000,000,000 electrons flow past a given point in one second of time, one ampere of current is flowing.

Now, then, what does a pencil or a piece of paper have to do with electricity? The answer, as you undoubtedly have surmised by now, is in the fact that all matter — pencils and paper or anything else — are made of molecules. The molecules, in turn, are built of atoms, and atoms have electrical charges of protons and electrons. When matter has an excess of either protons or electrons, it is said to have a charge which can be measured in coulombs, the symbol for which is Q. One coulomb — or one Q — has a charge of 6.28×10^{18} electrons. If a negatively charged body is connected to a positively charged body with a conductor, an electrical current will flow. Electrical current is the rate of electron flow past a given point in a unit of time. If one coulomb of electrons flows past a given point in one second of time one ampere of current is flowing.

REVIEW QUESTIONS

1. List ten things which are made of molecules.

2. Write your description of an atom.

3. List ten different elements.

4. Draw a diagram of a hydrogen atom, and name its parts.

5. Draw a diagram of an ion.

6. Draw a diagram of a charged atom.

7. Write the rule of electricity dealing with the attraction and repulsion of charges.

8. Draw a diagram showing what will happen if two atoms, which have the same charge, are brought near one another.

9. Draw a diagram showing what will happen if two atoms having unlike charges are brought near one another.

10. Write a brief description of 10 amperes.

11. Describe how an ampere differs from a coulomb.

12. Write the abbreviation of "ampere"; write its symbol; write the symbol for "charge"; write the symbol for "time."

13. Briefly describe an insulator.

14. Briefly describe a conductor.

15. Show, by diagram, what will happen if two oppositely charged pieces of matter are connected by a conductor.

Unit 2

It is one thing to know what electricity is, but quite another matter understanding it, and it is important to understand this wonderful force before one can intelligently use it to best advantage. To begin an understanding of electricity, *voltage* (*volt*-age) will be considered.

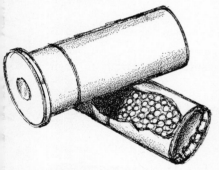

For just a moment forget electricity and consider something with which you are more familiar. If you have ever hunted ducks or pheasants you understand the construction of a shotgun shell with its hard-hitting steel pellets and explosive charge of gunpowder.

You know the pellets remain stored inside their round cardboard or plastic container until the hammer of the gun slams down upon the brass head of the shell. When this happens, the powder explodes and pushes the pellets out of the gun barrel at a speed of several hundred miles per hour.

Stop to consider the action. The gunpowder was stored in the shell, and even though it had tremendous explosive force or potential, nothing happened until the hammer of the shotgun snapped down. The pellets were also stored in the shell and remained there, unmoving until the potential charge exploded and exerted pressure behind the pellets pushing them forward through the gun barrel.

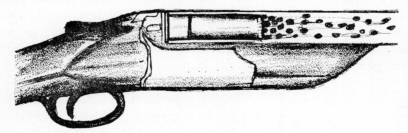

Potential Force

Strangely enough electricity is very much like a loaded shotgun shell. Electrons are comparable to the steel pellets of the shell. They are stationary and will never

11

flow unless acted upon by some potential force which will push them forward through a conductor. There must be some kind of "gunpowder" which will exert pressure on the electrons and push them along. Indeed, there *is* such a potential force; it is called voltage.

The more gunpowder there would be, the more pellets it could push out of the barrel of the gun. On the other hand, the more pressure that could be exerted upon the electrons, the more electrons would be pushed along a conductor.

In Unit 1 you learned that current is a flow of electrons in a given unit of time. You will remember current is measured in amperes and has the symbol *I*. Time, for most purposes, is measured in seconds and has the symbol "t."

REMEMBER
current = amperes = I
time = "t"

Difference in Charge

If current is a flow of electrons something must cause the electrons to begin to flow and to keep them moving. There must be a force of some kind pushing them along. This force is not gunpowder, but it is the *difference in the amount of charge* between two bodies. You will recall from Unit 1 that it is possible to charge neutral atoms by giving them an excess of electrons or protons. If an atom has an excess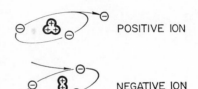

POSITIVE ION

NEGATIVE ION

of protons, it is positively charged. If it has an excess of electrons, it has a negative charge. It is this charge that causes electrons to flow, and more particularly it is the *difference* in charge that gets the job done.

Thus, if one object has a charge of +4 and another object has a charge of −4, there is a difference in charge. This difference provides the conditions necessary to set a current in motion, and if the difference in charge is maintained the current will continue to flow until the charge differential is removed. This difference in charge, then, is the potential, which compares with the gunpowder in the shotgun shell. Unless the force is somehow released it will remain dormant just as the gunpowder remained stored in the shell until the hammer snapped down.

SET ONE   SET TWO

A   B   C   D

Here is a problem to determine whether or not you have grasped the idea involved. Imagine you have two sets of objects, A and B, and also C and D. Compare objects A and B with one another, then compare objects C and D. When you have done that compare the two sets.

Suppose object *A* has a charge of +2 and object *B* a charge of −2. Further assume object *C* has a charge of +4 and object *D* a charge of −4. Which set will have the greatest difference in charge, *A* and *B* or *C* and *D*?

Immediately, you can tell *C* and *D* have the greatest difference in charge because they have the highest and lowest numbers, +4 and −4. Since they have the greatest charge, they will also have the most "push" and will therefore cause more electrons to flow than will set *A* and *B*. If *C* and *D* will push the most electrons, they thus cause the highest amperage.

Voltage Provides Pressure

Now, then, take one of the previous sets, *C* and *D*. The *difference* in charge represents the "gunpowder" or the potential. However, just like the gunpowder, this difference in potential will not "explode" until a conductor is placed between charge *C* and charge *D*. When this happens, the law of attraction and repulsion takes over. Since the charge on *C* and *D* are opposite there is an attraction. This attraction creates the "explosion" when the conductor provides a path over  which the charge can push the electrons. However, instead of pushing the electrons along at several hundreds of miles per hour, the electrons are shot along the wire at the speed of light — 186,000 miles per second.

How much difference is there between +4 and −4? There are 8 points of difference. You can easily plot this with a graph by drawing a vertical line and placing 0 (zero) at the center. Then, using some convenient length for spacing, such as quarter-inch intervals, step off equal distances above and below 0. Everything below 0 is minus (−) while everything above 0 is plus (+). Then, starting at the first division mark from the bottom and counting to the top mark, you will find 8 points difference.

Instead of talking about *points* of difference, provide a name for those points and call them *volts*. Voltage is the *potential,* or *push,* which can cause electrons to flow along a conductor. Volts or voltage has been given the symbol **V**.

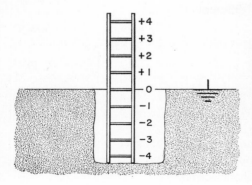

Ground Potential

Rather than using a straight vertical line, one might very well think of the line as being a ladder. Better yet, make it a ladder which is resting in a hole in the ground, but which has several rungs projecting above the surface of the ground. The ground line corresponds to the zero mark on the ladder, and since "zero" and "ground" are the same thing, one could correctly use either term. Persons dealing with electricity often refer to the term "ground," and speak of a zero charge of electricity as being at "ground potential." A special symbol has been designed for ground: ⏚

Voltage exists between *any* two charges which are not exactly equal. Even a neutral (uncharged) piece of matter has a potential difference when compared with a charged piece of matter — it is negative when compared with a positive charge, but positive when compared with a negative charge. Voltage is a *relative* thing, used to compare one charge with another.

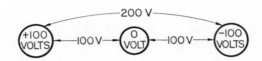

Which of the conditions below has the greater difference in charge?

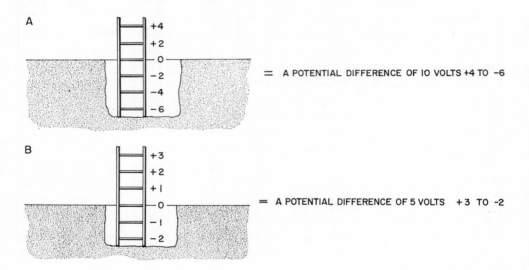

A = A POTENTIAL DIFFERENCE OF 10 VOLTS +4 TO −6

B = A POTENTIAL DIFFERENCE OF 5 VOLTS +3 TO −2

Condition *A* would have the greater differential.

Which of the following two conditions would have the greater difference?

As you can see, ladder *A* is 8 volts positive while ladder *B* is 8 volts negative. Even though one is positive and the other negative the fact remains each has a *potential difference* of 8 volts from ground. There would be a *total* potential difference of 16 volts from +8 to −8.

The ladder has provided a means for distinguishing between positive potential, negative potential, and ground. Other objects could also add to one's comprehension of voltage — the push behind the electron.

14

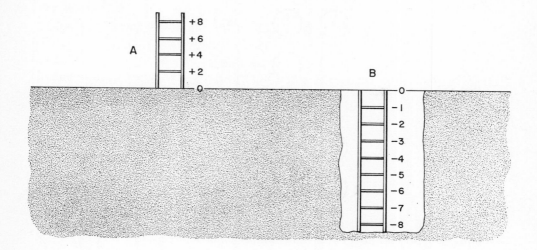

One could use aluminum balls as the objects. In this case, both *A* and *B* have charges. The charge for each is +1. Since there is no *difference* in potential between the two aluminum balls there would be no pressure (voltage) existing between them.

The same condition would exist if the charges on the two balls were as shown below:

$\left(\bigcirc{-}\right)_A$ & $\left(\bigcirc{-}\right)_B$ = NO VOLTAGE POTENTIAL

$\left(\bigcirc{+\atop+}\right)_A$ & $\left(\bigcirc{+}\right)_B$ = NO VOLTAGE POTENTIAL

$\left(\bigcirc{=}\right)_A$ & $\left(\bigcirc{=}\right)_B$ = NO VOLTAGE POTENTIAL

There are millions of other combinations.

But, notice what happens as soon as a *difference* exists between the two balls as shown below:

$\left(\bigcirc{+\atop+}\right)_A$ & $\left(\bigcirc{+}\right)_B$ = I VOLT

$\left(\bigcirc{-}\right)_A$ & $\left(\bigcirc{-}\right)_B$ = I VOLT

$\left(\bigcirc{=}\right)_A$ & $\left(\bigcirc{=}\right)_B$ = I VOLT

15

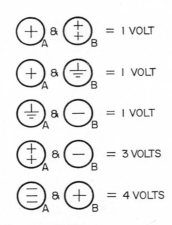

$\left(\begin{smallmatrix}+\end{smallmatrix}\right)_A$ & $\left(\begin{smallmatrix}+\\+\end{smallmatrix}\right)_B$ = 1 VOLT

$\left(\begin{smallmatrix}+\end{smallmatrix}\right)_A$ & $\left(\begin{smallmatrix}+\\=\end{smallmatrix}\right)_B$ = 1 VOLT

$\left(\begin{smallmatrix}=\end{smallmatrix}\right)_A$ & $\left(\begin{smallmatrix}-\end{smallmatrix}\right)_B$ = 1 VOLT

$\left(\begin{smallmatrix}+\\+\end{smallmatrix}\right)_A$ & $\left(\begin{smallmatrix}-\end{smallmatrix}\right)_B$ = 3 VOLTS

$\left(\begin{smallmatrix}=\\=\end{smallmatrix}\right)_A$ & $\left(\begin{smallmatrix}+\end{smallmatrix}\right)_B$ = 4 VOLTS

Now consider still another possibility:

Nothing can be said about the voltage *differential* between this and something else because the two positive charges on the ball are not *compared* with anything. The only state-  ment which can be made with a degree of honesty is simply that the ball has a charge of positive 2. It does *not* have a voltage difference of 2!

Balls can also be used to determine whether an object is positive or negative *with respect to a certain point*. Take a look at the following:

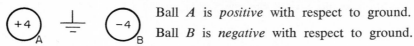

Ball *A* is *positive* with respect to ground.
Ball *B* is *negative* with respect to ground.

The above could be stated in slightly different terms:

Ball *A* is at a positive voltage with respect to ground.

Ball *B* is at a negative voltage with respect to ground.

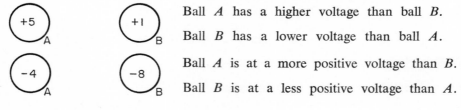

Ball *A* has a higher voltage than ball *B*.

Ball *B* has a lower voltage than ball *A*.

Ball *A* is at a more positive voltage than *B*.

Ball *B* is at a less positive voltage than *A*.

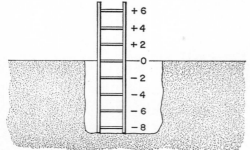

In determining the above relation- ships you should recall the ladder and its position above and below ground.

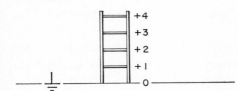

Thus:

The charge on *A* is more positive than on *B* (or less negative).
The charge on *C* is less positive than on *D* (or more negative).
The charge on *B* is more negative than on *A* (or less positive).
The charge on *D* is more positive than on *C* (or less negative).
The charge on *A* is more negative than on *E* (or less positive).
The charge on *E* is more positive than on *B* (or less negative).
The charge on *E* is less positive than on *C* (or more negative).

In all of the foregoing diagrams it was necessary to *compare* a particular point with another point before one could determine whether it was at a higher or lower potential.

Voltage Drop

Now consider still another concept — that of voltage *drop*. To what does this term refer?

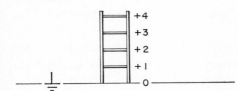

In order to understand this term more completely, once again go back to the ladder.

There is a *positive* voltage drop from +4 to +2 because it goes from a *higher* to a lower potential.

An object has a positive potential with respect to another object if it has a higher potential or position.

On the other hand, there is a negative or minus voltage drop from a low to a high potential.

Here there is a + potential *drop* from *A* to *B*, but a − potential *drop* from *B* to *A*.

Consider the following:

There is a +10-volt drop from *A* to *C*, but only a +4-volt drop from *A* to *B*.
There is a −10-volt drop from *C* to *A*, and a −6-volt drop from *C* to *B*.
There is a +2-volt drop from *C* to *D*, but a −2-volt drop from *D* to *C*.
There is a +14-volt drop from *A* to *E*, and a −12-volt drop from *D* to *A*.

From the foregoing you can readily see it is entirely possible for *one* particular point to be either positive *or* negative to some other point or points. On the preceding page point *D* (even though it is a negative number) is *positive* with respect to *E*, but *negative* with respect to point *C*!

The above is a very important concept for you to remember. It is used again and again and again in electronics. Technicians troubleshooting electronic apparatus of all kinds continually make use of this very important fact.

One can summarize all of the above by comparing electrical current to water. Water *always* flows from a higher to a lower point. Electrical current will also flow from a higher potential to a lower potential. That is, it will flow from a greater to a lesser charge.

Voltage Terminology

Thus far several terms have been used in connection with voltage. It has been called a force and a potential. It has been referred to in terms of voltage drop and as a pushing force. It has been stated that one symbol for voltage is *V*. Now it can be stated that another term is often used when speaking of voltage — *electromotive force*. Electromotive force is abbreviated to **e.m.f.** or simply **E**. Voltage, then may be either *V* or *E*.

Some people go so far as to differentiate between *V* and *E*. They think of *V* in terms of height such as its position on a ladder — this becomes potential. They refer to voltage *drop* as *V*.

When thinking of the symbol *E* some people think about electromotive force or e.m.f. They refer to the voltage of a battery or other source as *E*. To them, *E* is synonymous with *voltage rise*.

Many persons simply use *E* universally for *either V* or *E*. This practice is by far the most popular.

This chapter has dealt with understanding the principle of electricity known as *voltage*. Voltage is the force which pushes electrons along a conductor. Without voltage to exert pressure, electrons would remain in the conductor and would never form an electric current. To have amperage *one must have a voltage*. Without an *E* there would never be an *I*.

> **REMEMBER**
> Voltage == Pressure or Electromotive Force
> Voltage = E M F or E or V

A Possible Misconception

All of the concepts pointed out thus far are correct and will help one gain a useful knowledge of electricity. However, there is a possibility a misconception may have crept into the explanations because they have been simplified in order to make them more easily understandable. The student should not conclude from the preceding explanations that any one or two charged atoms have a *large* attraction or repulsion for one another. Such is *not* the case! In fact, it would require billions of ionized molecules to light a 40-watt bulb.

It has been estimated that 500 billion billion (500,000,000,000,000,000,000) neutral molecules are found in one cubic inch of air. If *all* of these billions of molecules each gave up an electron, they would produce only enough electricity to light a 40-watt bulb about three minutes.

REVIEW QUESTIONS

1. Write a brief description of *voltage*.

2. Diagram one ball having a +5 charge, and another ball with a −5 charge. Connect the two with a conductor and use an arrow to show the direction in which the electrons will flow.

3. Draw a ball diagram containing Figures *A, B, C, D,* and *E*. Ball *A* will have a charge of +2, ball *B* a charge of +1, ball *C* a charge of ground, ball *D* a charge of −1, and ball *E* a charge of −2.
   Complete the following table by crossing out the incorrect word:

   A is (higher lower) than B
   A is (higher lower) than C
   B is (higher lower) than D
   B is (higher lower) than A
   C is (higher lower) than A
   C is (higher lower) than D
   C is (higher lower) than B
   C is (higher lower) than E
   D is (higher lower) than A
   D is (higher lower) than E
   E is (higher lower) than C
   E is (higher lower) than A

4. Draw a ball diagram containing Figures *A, B, C, D,* and *E*. Ball *A* has a +5 charge, ball *B* has a +1 charge, ball *C* has a "0" charge, ball *D* has a −1 charge, and ball *E* has a −5 charge.
   Fill in the following table:

   There is a +5-volt drop from _____ to _____.
   There is a −5-volt drop from _____ to _____.
   There is a −1-volt drop from _____ to _____.
   There is a +6-volt drop from _____ to _____.

5. List five different terms or abbreviations which are synonyms for voltage.

Unit 3

CELLS AND BATTERIES

By now you know there are electrons contained in everything. Those materials having many *free electrons* are called conductors. Copper wire is a conductor and it is used for carrying electrical current in many electrical devices.

You also know that electrical current is a flow of electrons, and it is measured in amperes. However, electrons will not flow in a conductor of any kind unless there is a pressure — a voltage — pushing them, and there will never be a voltage created unless a difference in charge exists.

From where does this difference in charge come? Stating the problem in a slightly different way, what can one use to create this difference in charge which represents voltage — the pushing force for moving free electrons?

Battery — A Source of Voltage

A battery is one source of voltage (e.m.f.). It acts somewhat like the charge of gunpowder in the shotgun shell. That is, it is a potential which is "stored" and which will not be released until something happens to "trigger" the charge. In a shotgun shell the charge is released when the gun's hammer snaps down upon the shell; in a battery the charge is released when a wire conductor is connected between the positive and negative poles. In a shotgun shell the steel pellets are pushed through the gun barrel by the gunpowder charge; in a battery the electrons are pushed through the wire conductor by the difference in charge of the ionized atoms. In a shotgun shell an explosion will occur and stop just as suddenly as it started; in a battery hookup the charge will remain and electrons will continue to be pushed around the circuit until the battery wears out.

What, then, is a battery?

Metals are chock-full of free electrons, but some metals give up these electrons more readily than do other metals. Zinc, for example, will give up electrons more easily than copper. You will recall from Unit 1 that an atom which has lost one or more electrons acquires a positive charge because there will be more protons on the atom than electrons. Now then, if zinc gives up electrons faster than copper, it follows that zinc ions will be *more positive* than copper under the same conditions. This is true because zinc will then have more protons left within its makeup than copper will have.

But enough of these generalities! For a complete understanding of what actually happens, take a closer look at the ionization theory of battery action. In so doing you will be using all of the information you have thus far learned regarding attraction and repulsion, ionization, electrons, and protons. In addition to this you will become acquainted with some new words:

Electrolyte (ee-*leck*-tro-light) — a liquid which will pass an electric current. It is a conductor of electrons. Sulfuric acid dissolved in water is one example of many different kinds of electrolytes.

Sulfuric acid — a heavy, corrosive, oily liquid. The chemical symbol is H_2SO_4.

The Voltaic Cell

When an electrolyte, such as a mixture of sulfuric acid and water, is examined it is found that the sulfuric acid and water divided into ions.

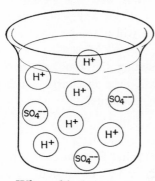

The positive and negative ions move about freely in the solution. The solution itself is *neutral* because there are equal numbers of positive and negative charges.

Thus, one molecule of sulfuric acid divides into two hydrogen ions H^+H^+ (with positive charges) and one sulfate ion SO_4 (with a double negative charge).

The two extra electrons on the sulfate ion were borrowed from the two hydrogen atoms.

When this information is written in the form of a chemical formula it appears as follows:

$$H_2SO_4 \rightarrow 2H^+ + SO_4^{--}$$

When a copper (Cu) and zinc (Zn) strip are placed in the electrolyte the zinc dissolves *faster* than copper. In so doing many of the zinc atoms readily go into the chemical solution and become ionized. When a zinc atom becomes a zinc ion it loses two electrons and becomes positive.

$$Zn^0 - 2e \rightarrow Zn^{++}$$

Even though some of the zinc has dissolved, the electrons *remain on the zinc strip* giving it a *negative charge*.

You will now recall that *like charges repel*. Since the zinc ions are positive, and since the hydrogen ions are *also* positive they will repel one another and the positive hydrogen ions will be driven away from the zinc strip.

22

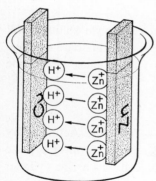

Remember, the zinc dissolved *faster* than the copper. When the zinc dissolved it formed negative electrons which remained on the strip. Since the *zinc* strip had an excess of negative electrons, the *copper* strip must have been *relatively* positive. The negative electrons attempted to get over to the relatively positive copper at their first opportunity.

Now, if the two strips are connected with a wire conductor the negative electrons will be attracted to the relatively positive copper strip. A current begins to flow!

As the negative electrons, being carried over the wire, strike the copper strip they will come into contact with the positive hydrogen ions which have been forced there from the zinc ions.

When that happens each hydrogen ion will pick up one electron and it will become a completed hydrogen *atom*.

$$H^+ \qquad + \qquad 1e \qquad \rightarrow \qquad H^0$$
(hydrogen ion) plus (one electron) yields (hydrogen atom)

The hydrogen atoms combine to form bubbles of hydrogen gas which collect on the copper strip. The chemical reaction will continue as long as there is a zinc strip to furnish zinc ions, and as long as there is acid to furnish hydrogen ions.

Local Action

Commercial zinc is not pure, but contains small amounts of cadmium, iron, and lead. Since these metals are different from zinc, zinc ions will dissolve into the solution at those points where the metal is the purest. Hydrogen ions will change into atoms near the impurities. A battery action is thus set up near the zinc strip and the zinc is used up without producing any useful potential at the regular poles of the battery. This *undesirable* action is called *local action*. To prevent this, zinc is coated with a layer of mercury and the zinc is then said to be "amalgamated." Amalgamation helps prevent local action.

Polarization

When the battery provides an electrical current, the potential of the battery drops sharply because of the hydrogen bubbles which form and cover the copper strip. These bubbles act as an insulator, preventing the electrolyte from getting to the copper strip. This action is called *polarization*. By adding an oxidizing agent, such as manganese dioxide, to a cell, the polarization is lessened. The oxygen atoms from the manganese dioxide combine with the hydrogen to form water, thus dissipating the hydrogen bubbles which would otherwise collect.

Battery Requirements

Any two dissimilar metals which are immersed in an electrolyte solution will form a battery. Different combinations of metals will provide different charges. If a continuous current is desired, the electrolyte which is used must attack one of the two metals more than the other.

Primary Cells

Primary cells are usually known by another name — *dry cells*. Actually dry cells are not dry, but have the electrolyte and depolarizer in the form of a paste instead of a liquid. This cell, also known as the Leclanche cell, has a zinc cylinder for the negative pole which serves double duty by also acting as the container. The positive pole is a carbon rod. The rod is surrounded by a mixture of finely divided carbon and manganese dioxide which acts as the depolarizer. Between the depolarizer and the zinc container is a 25 percent solution of ammonium chloride and another substance which helps keep it in paste form. The material mixed with the ammonium chloride is often charcoal, gypsum, paper pulp, or sawdust. Glycerine, zinc chloride, calcium chloride are sometimes added to help keep the cell moist. Since the cell cannot be successfully recharged, it is referred to as a primary cell. Its potential is 1.5 volts.

Secondary Cells

Secondary cells are often known by another name — *storage cells*. Actually these cells do not store electricity, but instead store the chemicals which cause the reaction that provides the potential. The battery is made of plates which in turn are made of lead (Pb) and lead peroxide (PbO_2). Since lead and lead peroxide are two dissimilar materials, one of the necessities of a cell or battery has been met. The plates are immersed in an electrolyte solution of water and sulfuric acid.

When the secondary cell is first manufactured the plates are made of *one* type of metal — lead. However, before it can be used as a cell the plates must be "formed" by passing a direct current through the plates and electrolyte. This charging current creates the two dissimilar materials by means of chemical action, and a voltaic cell is "made" electrically. Because the cell is not "used up" as it discharges, but merely changes chemical structure, it can again be recharged with a direct current, and it is therefore called a *secondary cell* to distinguish it from the primary. Its potential is 2.2 volts per cell.

The electrolytes used are either an acid or an alkali. Most primary cells now in use employ zinc and carbon poles and an alkaline electrolyte of ammonium chloride; ammonium chloride is more commonly known as sal-ammoniac. Secondary cells usually use lead for the poles and a solution of sulfuric acid for the electrolyte.

Cells and Batteries

At this point it is well to distinguish between a cell and a battery. Correctly, a battery does not become a true battery until two or more *cells* are connected together.

One 1½-volt flashlight cell is *not* a battery, nor is a large 1½-volt telephone-type cell a battery. One could have a cell as large as a wastebasket and it still would be considered a 1½-volt *cell*. Not until *two or more cells* are connected together do they become a battery!

Schematic (*skee*-ma-tic) symbols for cells and batteries are as follows:

Schematic symbol for a cell.

Schematic symbol for a battery.

This is a cell.

These are cells.

This is a battery of cells.

Connecting Batteries

If you had two 6-volt batteries, how would you connect them to form a 12-volt battery? How would you connect them to have a 6-volt battery that would last *twice as long* as one alone?

Series Connections

When batteries are connected in *series* (*seer*-eez), the positive pole of one is connected to the negative pole of another. By connecting the negative pole of one battery to the positive pole of another the voltage of one adds to the voltage of the other.

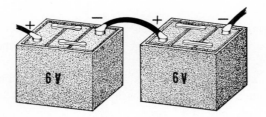

BATTERIES CONNECTED
IN SERIES ADD VOLTAGE

This connection does *not* add voltage because the two negative poles are connected together.

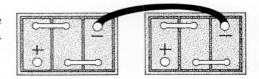

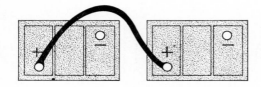

This connection does *not* add voltage because the two positive poles are connected together.

In this connection, the two batteries do add voltage, but a *short circuit* exists because there is a completed circuit between all *four* poles without having a high enough resistance in the circuit. The wires will overheat and the batteries will be ruined.

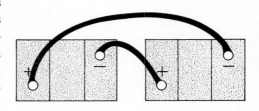

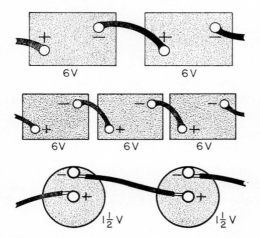

THIS CONNECTION PROVIDES 12 VOLTS.

THIS CONNECTION PROVIDES 18 VOLTS.

THIS CONNECTION PROVIDES 3 VOLTS.

26

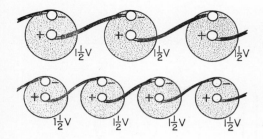

THIS CONNECTION PROVIDES $4\frac{1}{2}$ VOLTS.

THIS CONNECTION PROVIDES 6 VOLTS.

Parallel Connections

When batteries or cells are connected in *parallel* (*pair*-a-lel) positive poles are connected together and negative poles are connected together.

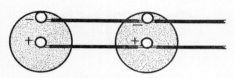

Batteries connected in parallel do *not* add voltage, but they do add the total amount of amperage available. Here are two cells connected in parallel — they add amperage.

By connecting the negative pole of one battery or cell to the negative pole of another, and the positive pole to the remaining positive pole, the two batteries or cells will last twice as long as one alone.

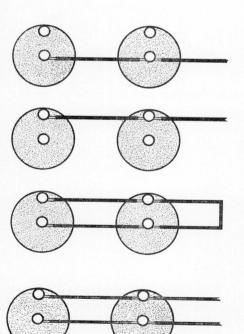

This connection does *not* add amperage because the two negative poles are not connected.

This connection does *not* add amperage because the two positive poles are not connected.

In this connection the two cells *do* add amperage, but a *short circuit* exists because there is a completed circuit with a common wire. The wires will overheat and the cells will be ruined.

THIS CONNECTION PROVIDES 36 AMPERES.

18 A   18 A

THIS CONNECTION PROVIDES 54 AMPERES.

18 A   18 A   18 A

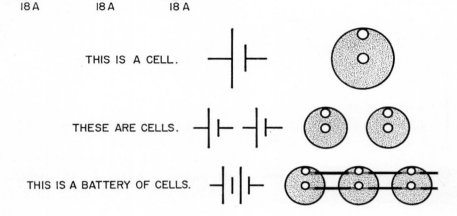

THIS IS A CELL.

THESE ARE CELLS.

THIS IS A BATTERY OF CELLS.

Series-Parallel Connections

One can take advantage of both series and parallel connections in connecting batteries or cells.

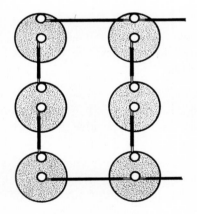

This connection provides 4½ volts at 36 amperes. Can you determine why?

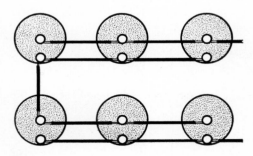

This connection provides 3 volts at 54 amperes. Can you determine why?

Opposing Voltages

Cells and batteries may also be connected in such a manner that voltages subtract. However, this is almost never practiced, and is included here for purposes of illustration only.

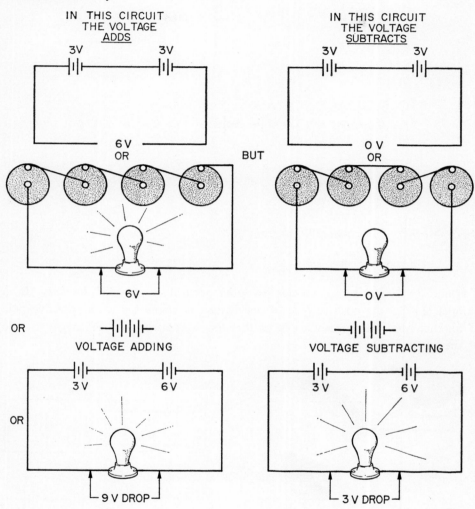

■ A Problem for You

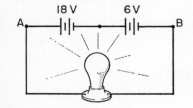

How much voltage will be available at points *A* and *B*? (Answer: 24 volts.)

How much voltage drop will occur across the lamp? (Answer: 24 volts.)

How can one subtract voltages without securing a parallel hookup? In a parallel hookup the positive pole of one battery is connected to the positive pole of another, *and* the negative pole of the first is connected to the negative pole of the other. Thus:

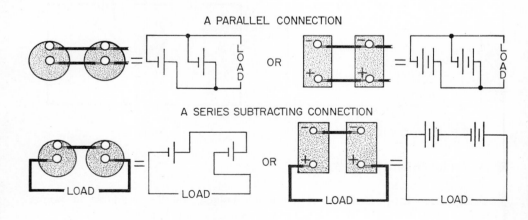

A PARALLEL CONNECTION

A SERIES SUBTRACTING CONNECTION

REVIEW QUESTIONS

1. Write a brief definition for *electrolyte*.

30

2. Each of the following cells has a voltage of 1.5 and an amperage of 18 amperes. Wire them in such a manner that you will secure 6 volts at 18 amperes.

3. Each of the following cells has a voltage of 1.5 volts and an amperage of 18 amperes. Wire them in such a manner that you will secure 1.5 volts at 54 amperes.

4. Each of the following cells has a voltage of 1.5 volts and an amperage of 18 amperes. Wire them in such a manner that you will secure 4.5 volts at 36 amperes.

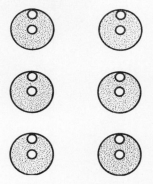

5. Each of the following cells has a voltage of 1.5 volts and an amperage of 18 amperes. Wire them in series-opposing.

LOAD

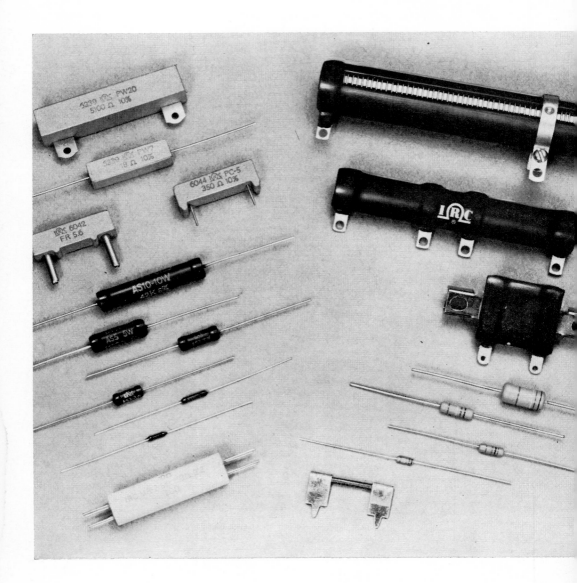

Unit 4

In Unit 3 various battery connections were shown which provided different combinations of voltage and amperage. As a means for introducing still another electrical phenomenon, *resistance* (ree-*zis*-tans), the battery will again be used.

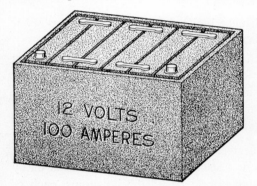

Suppose you have a battery capable of delivering 12 volts at 100 amperes. Does this mean the battery will actually exert a pressure of 12 volts upon the circuit in which it is connected? *Yes!* Does it also mean the battery will deliver 100 amperes to that same circuit? *Not necessarily!* How can this be?

The battery has 100 amperes *available* that *can be used* if needed.

What will determine how much amperage is used?

The total resistance in the circuit determines the amount of amperage used.

What is resistance? Resistance is an opposing action that limits, controls, or holds back the flow of electrons for a given voltage. The larger the resistance, the less will be the amperage for a particular voltage. The abbreviation for resistance is **R** and the schematic symbol is

From where does resistance come?

Some atoms hold onto their electrons only loosely, permitting them to flow rather freely. Other atoms are more stingy! They hang onto the electrons and do not permit them to flow freely through the conductor — at least not as readily.

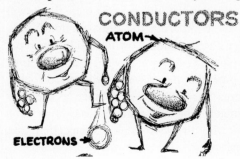

Any material which easily gives up its electrons is called a *conductor*. Metals such as aluminum, copper, silver, and iron are conductors. All of these do not conduct electrons equally well. Aluminum, for example, is a better conductor than iron, copper is a better conductor than aluminum, and silver is the best conductor of all.

33

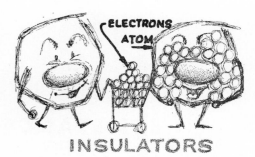

ELECTRONS

ATOM

INSULATORS

Materials made of atoms which hold on to their electrons are *insulators.* Glass, porcelain, rubber, and plastic are all insulators. Some insulators are better than others because they hang onto the electrons more tightly and therefore do not permit them to flow and form an amperage.

There are some materials called *semiconductors.* These permit more electrons to flow than do insulators, but they are still not considered good conductors.

Factors Affecting Resistance

Even good conductors have some resistance limiting the flow of electrons. Four factors affect the resistance of any conductor:

1. *Material.* The material from which the conductor is made directly affects the resistance. Silver is the best conductor known, next comes copper, aluminum, and so on. They are all metals and all conductors; however, if one were to check the resistance of each he would find aluminum had the highest resistance and silver the least, of the three named.

2. *Length.* Another factor affecting the resistance of a conductor is its length. The longer the conductor, the more resistance it will have. This is easily understood if one imagines the conductor to be filled with atoms, each of which has a very thin coating of glue. As the tiny electrons make their way between the atoms, some are sure to become stuck to the glue, and the longer the conductor the more chance there is for more electrons to get stuck.

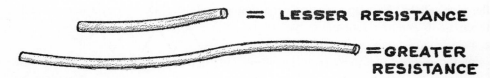

= LESSER RESISTANCE

= GREATER RESISTANCE

3. *Cross-sectional area.* The larger the diameter of a wire the less the resistance. The smaller the cross-sectional area the more resistance there will be. One can readily grasp this idea by comparing the cross-sectional area with a water pipe, and the electrons with the water flowing inside the pipe. The smaller the diameter of a water pipe, the less water will be able to flow. On the other hand, the larger the pipe the more water will get through. A pipe with a small cross-sectional area has a greater resistance to the flow of water than a pipe of a larger diameter. The very same is true of wire or any other conductor. The larger the wire the less the resistance, and the smaller the wire the greater is its resistance.

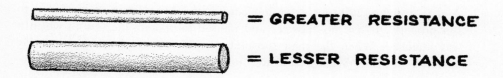

= **GREATER RESISTANCE**

= **LESSER RESISTANCE**

4. *Temperature.* The fourth factor affecting resistance is the temperature of the conductor. In most materials the higher the temperature the greater will be the resistance. This is true of all metals.

With some conductors, of a nonmetallic nature (such as carbon, metallic oxides, and other semiconductors), the higher the temperature the *lower* the resistance.

Generally speaking, however, the higher the temperature the greater the resistance.

The four factors mentioned are directly related to resistance, and must be considered whenever constructing or designing electrical apparatus. Still another factor, light, must sometimes be considered. The resistivity of selenium, for example, is affected by light. Since this course will not deal in photoelectricity, this factor will not be further considered.

The Unit of Resistance

The unit of resistance is the *ohm* (O-mm). It gets its name in honor of Georg Simon Ohm, the man who first discovered the mathematical relationship between voltage, resistance, and amperage. Using his law one can determine the third quantity if the other two are known. For example, if one knew the amount of available voltage and the amount of resistance present, he could calculate the amount of amperage which would flow in the circuit. This is an important consideration when designing a circuit and determining the size of wire to be used, the rating of fuses, and many other factors important to the proper operation of an electrical circuit.

For the person who is scientifically minded the ohm can be technically defined as the amount of resistance offered by a column of mercury 106.3 millimeters in length and 1 square millimeter in cross section. This roughly corresponds to the amount of resistance offered by 150 feet of 18-gauge copper wire.

The symbol for an ohm is: Ω

See whether you can name the factor involved in the following examples dealing with resistance:

1. When a glass rod was placed across the poles of a battery no current flowed, but a piece of copper wire connected to the same battery permitted a heavy amperage. What factor was involved?

35

2. A man using a 200-foot extension cord found his electric motor failed to run properly. It had no "power" and refused to operate the saw to which it was attached. When the man substituted a 25-foot cord the motor easily operated the saw. What factor was involved?

3. A student was experimenting with different sizes of wire. He found that one length of *fine* wire would barely permit a light bulb to glow when connected to a battery. On the other hand, another heavier wire, the same length, lighted the bulb at normal brilliance.

4. A radio repairman noticed that as he first turned a radio to the "on" position the tubes flared up and gave off considerable light, but as the set warmed up and continued to operate the glow in the tubes became dimmer and dimmer.

Kinds of Resistors

It would be impossible to name all of the kinds of resistors known to man, for there are as many resistors as their are conductors. *Anything* which carries an electrical current is a resistor.

TOASTERS ARE
RESISTORS

LIGHT BULBS
ARE RESISTORS.

RADIO CIRCUITS
ARE RESISTORS.

Special Resistors

Every radio and television set has special devices specifically called "resistors." These are used to limit or control the amount of current which will flow in particular parts of the circuit. These may be resistors having a fixed resistance which does not change under regular operating conditions, or they may be variable resistors which may be varied by the user.

This book will concern itself only with the fixed carbon resistor which is constructed of a rod of compressed graphite mixed with a binding material. The outer surface of the rod may then be painted or covered by an insulating coating of one kind or another. The leads attached to either end of the resistor are called pigtail leads.

There are two types of fixed carbon resistors.

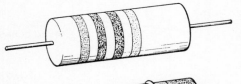

The *axial* (*axe*-ee-all) *lead* resistor has leads protruding from each end. This type is by far the most popular.

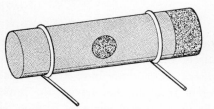

The *radial* (*ray*-dee-all) *lead* resistor has the leads wrapped around the body of the resistor.

The value of the resistor — the ohms rating — is either stamped on the body or different colors identify the resistance value. Usually the latter method is used.

Identifying Value of Axial Resistors

Identifying the value of resistance on an axial-lead resistor is a simple matter. To do so, hold the resistor by its two pigtail leads, with the color bands to the left. The color bands are then "read" from the left end toward the center. Each color has a particular number associated with it.

Color	Number
Black	0
Brown	1
Red	2
Orange	3
Yellow	4
Green	5
Blue	6
Violet	7
Gray	8
White	9

The first band from the left indicates the first digit.

The second band from the left indicates the second digit.

The third band from the left indicates the number of ciphers (zeros) to be added.

If there is a fourth band, it will be either silver or gold, and it indicates the tolerance.

Putting all of this information together provides the ohms value of the resistor:

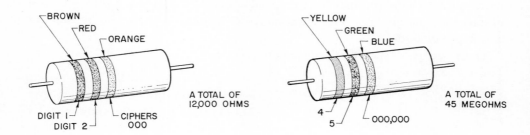

Tolerance Markings

When resistors are manufactured, it is practically impossible to manufacture each and every resistor so it will have precisely the same resistance. For this reason a resistor having the color code *brown-red-orange* may have a true resistance value which could be considerably different from another having the same coding. It could have a measured resistance as low as 9600 ohms or as high as 14,400 ohms.

How is this possible?

If the resistor contains only three color bands the manufacturer simply states that he has attempted to make a resistor which is as close to the indicated value as he possibly could. However, he does not guarantee the value, and in fact the only guarantee he makes is that it is within *20 percent* of the resistance value indicated by the color bands. Thus, a resistor having a banding of *brown-red-orange* indicates it is as near 12,000 ohms as manufacturing processes would permit it to be, but it may be as much as 2400 ohms off one way or the other.

Thus: $20\% \times 12,000 = 2400$ ohms

2400 ohms added to or subtracted from the indicated 12,000 ohms could be as little as a minimum of 9600 ohms to as much as 14,400 ohms. Usually, of course, it is much closer to the 12,000-ohm value than either the maximum or minimum.

Some applications of electronics demand a more precise tolerance. As a result of this, manufacturers had to choose their resistors more carefully. They finally decided upon two other color bands — silver and gold. A silver color band, found in the fourth position from the left, indicates a tolerance of 10 percent, while a gold band indicates a tolerance of 5 percent.

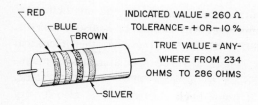

RED
BLUE
BROWN

INDICATED VALUE = 260 Ω
TOLERANCE = + OR – 10 %
TRUE VALUE = ANY-
WHERE FROM 234
OHMS TO 286 OHMS

SILVER

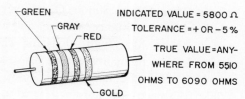

GREEN
GRAY
RED

INDICATED VALUE = 5800 Ω
TOLERANCE = + OR – 5 %
TRUE VALUE = ANY-
WHERE FROM 5510
OHMS TO 6090 OHMS

GOLD

Physical Size

The physical size of a resistor has nothing whatever to do with its amount of resistance. Its physical size is related to how much heat the resistor will dissipate. This will be thoroughly covered in a later chapter.

Radial-Lead Resistors

Radial-lead resistors use the same color code as the axial-lead, but instead of using color bands a slightly different method is used.

The method for reading the resistance of a radial-lead resistor is as follows:

First — read the color of the *body*.

Second — read the color of the *end*.

Third — read the color of the *dot*.

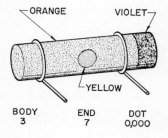

ORANGE   VIOLET

YELLOW

BODY	END	DOT
3	7	0,000

RESISTANCE = 370,000 OHMS

REMEMBER

The sequence for a radial-lead resistor:

BODY — END — DOT

Resistance Review

Resistance is a limiting or controlling factor. It holds back the flow of electrons. The greater the amount of resistance, the less will be the amperage for a given amount of voltage. Several factors affect resistance: (1) the kind of material, (2) the length of the material, (3) the cross-sectional area, and (4) the temperature. A long wire having a small cross-sectional area, and being hot, will have a greater resistance than a shorter wire having a larger cross-sectional area and being at a cooler temperature. Resistance is abbreviated to R and has a schematic symbol ⌇⌇⌇ . The unit of resistance is the ohm, named after Georg Simon Ohm, the first man to discover the mathematical relationship of resistance, voltage, and amperage. Any conductor is also a resistor, and therefore light bulbs, toasters, electric motors, and every other electrical device known to man are also resistors. There are also special resistors manufactured which are many times color coded to indicate their resistance value. While resistance is a nuisance because it holds back electrons, it is also a very necessary phenomenon because it provides a means of limiting or controlling the flow of electrons. The greater the resistance, the less the amperage for a given voltage.

REVIEW QUESTIONS

1. Briefly define *resistance*.

2. What happens to amperage if resistance increases and voltage remains constant?

3. What happens to amperage if resistance decreases and voltage remains constant?

4. Name four factors which will increase resistance.

5. What is the unit of resistance?

6. What is an abbreviation for resistance?

7. What is the schematic symbol for resistance?

8. Name ten resistors.

9. List the color code for resistors for all of the digits, going from 0 to 9.

10. Determine the resistance of the following axial-lead resistors:
    a) Brown, black, red
    b) Red, red, red
    c) Red, violet, orange, silver
    d) Blue, gray, yellow, gold

11. Determine the resistance of the following radial-lead resistors:
    a) Body — brown, end — black, dot — red
    b) Dot — red, body — green, end — blue
    c) End — white, dot — orange, body — brown
    d) Body — yellow, end—violet, dot— orange

12. Explain why a "tolerance" color is many times used on a resistor.

13. If a resistor has a color coding representing 1000 ohms, and it contains a silver band, what is the minimum and maximum resistance that resistor may have?

14. If a resistor has a color coding representing 1000 ohms, and it contains a gold band, what is the minimum and maximum resistance which that resistor may have?

Unit 5

WORK AND POWER

Force makes things move. It may be either a push or a pull — an attraction or a repulsion. When dealing with mechanical devices one is dealing with pushing and pulling. When dealing with electrical devices, the forces are attractions and repulsions.

Mechanical Force

Mechanical force is measured in pounds. If a student pushes on a weight suspended from a rope he will exert less force than he will when trying to push the same weight resting upon the floor. The weight on the rope has considerably less resistance hanging in the air than it has resting upon the floor.

If the student manages to push the weight across the floor a distance of 1 foot, a certain amount of mechanical work has been accomplished. If he pushes against the weight with a force of 10 pounds, and if he pushes it a distance of 1 foot, he can say he has done 10 foot-pounds of work. Foot-pounds is the unit in which mechanical work is measured.

Potential Force

One can also do work by lifting a weight. If a student lifts a 10-pound weight a height of 1 foot he has again done 10 foot-pounds of *mechanical* work. If he lifts the same weight 5 feet, he has accomplished 50 foot-pounds of work (5 × 10). He has expended energy by lifting it, and because he has lifted the weight to a particular height it is possible the weight may someday fall. Because of this possibility the energy he expended in lifting it is called a special kind of mechanical energy — *potential energy* (poe-*ten*-shul energy). It represents stored energy and it will remain stored until somehow released.

REMEMBER

Voltage is ELECTRICAL potential.

Dynamite conceals a considerable quantity of potential energy. The shotgun shell considered earlier also has potential energy, and a battery conceals potential energy. All of these can do work if the potential is released.

Joules

In electricity work is measured in *joules* (joo-els).

THE FORMULA

$$W = VQ$$

$$W = V \times Q$$

$$JOULES = VOLTS \times COULOMBS$$

When a charge is moved work is done.

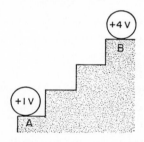

Moving a + charge from *A* to *B* requires work.

More work is required to move a positive charge to a high potential than it takes to move it to a lower potential.

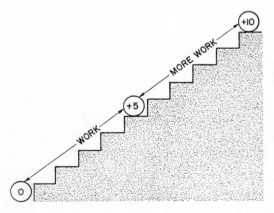

44

If 5 coulombs are moved across 2 volts, 10 joules of work has been accomplished:

$$\text{Work} = \text{Volts} \times \text{Coulombs}$$
$$W = V Q$$
$$= 2 \times 5$$
$$= 10 \text{ joules}$$

Work

Work is accomplished whenever a force causes motion. If motion never takes place under force there will never be any work accomplished. For example, a spring under tension may represent considerable force, but unless the spring's tension is released work is never accomplished. The powder in a shotgun shell represents force, but unless exploded no work is done. Also, a battery represents electrical force that *can* do work if and when that force is released.

The battery represents voltage, and voltage is an electrical force which can cause electrons to flow. The flow of electrons represents work. The *rate* at which that work is accomplished is called *electric power*.

REMEMBER

Power is the RATE of doing WORK.

Watts

The unit of electrical power is the *watt*. One horsepower is equivalent to 746 watts. Because a watt is a relatively small unit of measurement, the kilowatt is often used. The kilowatt is equal to 1000 watts.

REMEMBER

1 H.P. = 746 watts
1 kilowatt = 1000 watts

The abbreviation for wattage is **W,** but many times the letter **P** is used to denote *power*. To secure electrical power, volts are multiplied times amperes.

THE FORMULA

$$\mathbf{W} = \mathbf{E} \quad \mathbf{I} \quad \text{or}$$

WATTS = VOLTS × AMPERES

It is not difficult to understand *why* power is the product of voltage times amperage when one considers that voltage is a *force* which causes motion of electrons, and that amperage is the *rate* of electron flow. The force (voltage) causes the motion of electrons (work) in a given unit of time.

Remember: 1 ampere is equivalent to 1 coulomb flowing past a given point in 1 second, being pushed by a force of 1 volt.

And 1 volt times 1 ampere equals 1 watt.

From the foregoing one can see many concepts have been wrapped up into one neat package:

> *Force* causes things to move.
> *Voltage* is a force.
> *Work* is done when force causes motion.
> *Joules* are electrical units of work.
> *Amperage* represents rate of electron flow.
> *Power* is the rate of doing work.
> *Watts* are electrical units of power.

One may wonder where the term "horsepower" came from and what it has to do with power as described above. James Watt, inventor of the steam engine, needed some unit of measurement which would describe the power of his engines in terms people of that day would understand. He determined that a horse working all day could produce 33,000 foot-pounds of work per minute or 550 foot-pounds of work per second. He then compared this work output with that of his steam engines and people readily understood the comparison.

Mr. Watt also estimated that a man working all day could *average* ⅐ of 1 horsepower. For a short period he could turn out more than ⅐ of 1 horsepower, but it would then be necessary for him to rest, thus bringing his average down.

Watt's concept of horsepower has been handed down to present times and even now the electric motor is rated in horsepower, and 1 horsepower is equal to 746 watts.

THE FORMULA

$$W = E \quad I$$

WATTS (POWER) = VOLTS × AMPERES

REVIEW QUESTIONS

1. What is it that makes things move?
2. Mechanical force is measured in _____.
3. The unit of mechanical work is measured in _____ _____.
4. Electrical force is measured in_____.
5. In electricity, work is measured in _____.

6. A coulomb represents how many electrons?

7. To find joules one must multiply volts times _____.

8. Power is the _____ of doing work.

9. Work is accomplished whenever a force causes _____.

10. The unit of electrical power is the _____.

11. When one speaks of coulombs *per second* he is speaking of _____.

12. How many watts are equivalent to one horsepower?

13. To find watts one must multiply volts times _____.

14. If a student lifts a 10-pound weight 2 feet off the ground, how much work has he accomplished?

15. If 5 coulombs are moved across 6 volts, how much work has been accomplished?

16. A motor which requires 100 volts for normal operation and which draws 3.73 amperes will develop how much wattage?

17. The above motor will develop how much horsepower?

18. Three thousand watts is equivalent to how many kilowatts?

19. One thousand five hundred watts is equivalent to how many kilowatts?

20. How much more work will be required to lift 10 coulombs from 0 to 10 volts than it will to lift 10 coulombs from 0 to 5 volts?

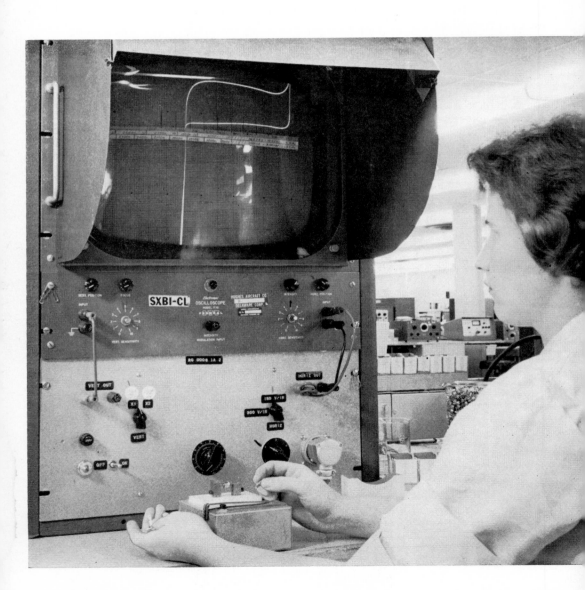

Unit 6

UNDERSTANDING NUMBERS

EQUATIONS AND FORMULAS

Anyone having a genuine interest in electricity will want to accomplish more than scratch the surface, yet it is impossible to gain any depth in understanding unless one deals with numbers. Some students make an earnest attempt at comprehending electrical principles without using numbers, but they ultimately find themselves far short of their desired goals.

Numbers are not difficult to work with. If properly presented and if used to solve problems of practical worth, numbers are fun to use and open new worlds of understanding for any subject.

What is the answer to the following problem?

$$5 \times 6 = ?$$

Of course you know the answer is 30. *But,* did you know you were working with an *equation* (ee-*kway*-shun) when you solved for the answer? You were indeed.

$5 \times 6 = 30$ is an equation! The left side of the equal sign equals the right side. $\frac{1}{2} + \frac{1}{2} = 30$ is *not* an equation. The two sides are not equal.

Letters can be substituted for numbers and one would still have an equation:

$$I \times R = E \qquad \text{where} \begin{cases} I = 5 \\ R = 6 \\ E = 30 \end{cases}$$

In writing equations it is not necessary to use the "times" sign ($\times$). Writing one letter immediately next to another means the two are multiplied.

$$I\,R = E \quad \text{is the same as} \quad I \times R = E$$

$I\,R = E$ could also be stated as $E = I\,R$ because $5 \times 6 = 30$ is the same as $30 = 5 \times 6$.

Transposing Letters

Assume you have the following equation:

$$E = I\,R$$

Now, assume you know the value of *E* and *I,* but you do *not* know *R.* The problem, then, is to change the *formula* (equation) in such a manner that it will enable you to solve for *R.*

49

Stating this another way, you wish to have *R* stand alone on one side of the equation:

$$R = ? \quad or \quad ? = R$$

Basic Formula

To accomplish this go back to the original formula, the basic formula, E = I R. In order to have *R* stand alone on the right side of the equal sign one would simply have to divide by *I,* thus:

$$E = \frac{\cancel{I}\,R}{\cancel{I}}$$

The two *I*'s cancel out and the *R* stands alone. *But wait!* There is a rule in working with formulas which states that whatever is done with one side of an equation must *also* be done with the other side. So, *your work is not complete.* *Both sides* of the formula *should have been divided by I:*

$$\frac{E}{I} = \frac{\cancel{I}\,R}{\cancel{I}} \quad or \quad \frac{E}{I} = R$$

Converting the letters to the *numbers* originally used one would have:

$$\frac{E}{I} = R \quad or \quad \frac{30}{5} = R$$

So: R = 6

Practical Problems

Numbers are of little value if they are simply going to be played with. To make them meaningful numbers should solve actual problems.

Assume you have the following problem:

■ Problem 1

A battery is connected to a light bulb with an ammeter connected in series with the hookup.

The battery is 30 volts.

The ammeter indicates 5 amperes of current flowing.

What is the resistance of the light bulb?

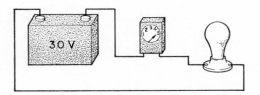
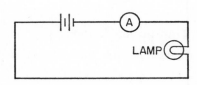

You know the *basic formula* is E = I R.

It is necessary to have the *R* stand alone since it is the unknown. The formula must be changed:

Change $E = IR$ to $\dfrac{E}{I} = \dfrac{\cancel{I}\,R}{\cancel{I}}$ or $\dfrac{E}{I} = R$

then substitute the known values:

$$\dfrac{30}{5} = 6 \text{ ohms of resistance}$$

↟

Your answer

■ Problem 2

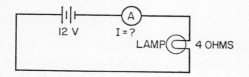

Basic Formula: $E = IR$

Since you are looking for *I*, it must stand alone. *R* must be moved to the other side of the equation.

Change $E = IR$ to $\dfrac{E}{R} = \dfrac{I\,\cancel{R}}{\cancel{R}}$ or $\dfrac{E}{R} = I$

Substitute values $\dfrac{12}{4} = I$ or 3 amperes

■ Problem 3

Basic Formula: $E = IR$

In this problem it is not necessary to change the formula. Why? You are solving for *E*, and *E* already stands alone on one side of the formula.

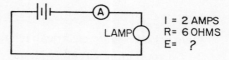

You simply need to substitute values and solve the problem:

$$E = IR$$
$$E = 2 \times 6$$
$$E = 12 \text{ volts}$$

Word Problems

Besides changing the basic formula $E = IR$ to provide an equation that would solve the problem involved, you were unconsciously doing something else. You were working *word problems*. What is meant by this? Go back to Problem 1.

In this problem you were *really* being asked this question:

What must be the resistance of the light bulb if it takes 30 volts to push 5 amperes of current through the circuit?

In Problem 2 you were being asked this question:

If 12 volts of pressure are being forced against 4 ohms of resistance, how much amperage will flow in the circuit?

Problem 3 posed this question:

If 2 amperes of current are flowing in a circuit having 6 ohms of resistance, what must be the voltage pushing the current?

OHM'S LAW

It is certainly not difficult to see that word problems are long and difficult to handle. It is much easier to reduce word problems to a kind of electrical "shorthand." This electrical shorthand is the given formulas and equations, all three of which can be worked by memorizing only *one* formula — the *basic formula*.

THE FORMULA

$$E = I R$$

This is not all. True, you have learned how to change one basic formula into a total of three. It is also true you have seen how it is possible to reduce lengthy word problems into simple electrical shorthand. But you have also learned something else that is very important. You have been working with a law of electricity.

REMEMBER

OHM'S LAW ➡ Named in honor of Georg Simon Ohm, the man who invented the formula in 1827.

Ohm's Law states electrical relationships. These relationships are as follows:
1. Current in a circuit will *increase* providing the voltage is increased and resistance remains the same.
2. Current in a circuit will *decrease* if the resistance is increased and voltage is held constant.

If you wish to be very scientific about the two statements above you can state them in mathematical language:

THE RULE

Current flowing in a circuit is directly proportional to the applied voltage, and inversely proportional to the resistance.

Or, you can write the formulas in words instead of using letters:

Voltage equals *current* times *resistance*

or current equals voltage (electromotive force) divided by resistance

or resistance equals voltage (electromotive force) divided by amperes (current).

In effect Ohm's Law says:

It takes 1 volt to push 1 ampere through 1 ohm of resistance.

Summary

■ Problem 1 (Voltage)

Find the voltage when the amperage and resistance are known.

Given: I = 2 amperes
          R = 3 ohms
          E = ?

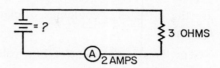

Basic formula: E = I R
Transposing (not necessary)
Substitute and solve: E = I R
                        E = 2 × 3
                        E = 6 volts

What the problem means: 6 volts of pressure are required to push 2 amperes of current through 3 ohms of resistance.

■ Problem 2 (Amperage)

Find the amperage when the voltage and resistance are known.

Given: I = ?
          R = 2 ohms
          E = 6 volts

Basic formula: E = I R

Transposing: $\dfrac{E}{R} = \dfrac{I \cancel{R}}{\cancel{R}}$ *or* $\dfrac{E}{R} = I$

Substitute and solve: $I = \dfrac{E}{R}$ *or* $I = \dfrac{6}{2}$ *or*   I = 3 amperes

What the problem means: 6 volts of electromotive force are required to push 3 amperes through 2 ohms of resistance.

NOTE: It is interesting to note the voltage in the second problem was the same as in the one above, but the amperage *increased* because the resistance *decreased*.

■ Problem 3 (Resistance)

Find the resistance when voltage and amperage are known.

Given: I = 2 amperes
          R = ?
          E = 6 volts

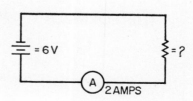

Basic formula: $E = IR$

Transposing: $\dfrac{E}{I} = \dfrac{\cancel{I}R}{\cancel{I}}$ *or* $\dfrac{E}{I} = R$

Substitute and solve: $R = \dfrac{E}{I}$ *or* $R = \dfrac{6}{2}$ *or* $R = 3$ ohms

What the problem means: 6 volts of electromotive force are required to push 2 coulombs of electrons through 3 ohms of resistance. (*Remember:* 2 amperes are the same as 2 coulombs of charge flowing past a given point in one second of time.)

NOTE: This is the same as the voltage problem on the preceding page but it is stated in different terms.

Things to Remember

REMEMBER

OHM'S LAW STATES

It takes 1 volt of pressure to push 1 ampere through 1 ohm of resistance.

Current in a circuit will increase providing the voltage increases and resistance remains the same.

Current in a circuit will decrease providing the resistance is increased and voltage is held constant.

TIME, CHARGE, AND CURRENT

The amount of current flowing in a conductor depends upon the amount of charge and the amount of time the charge flows.

Charge = Coulombs = Q
Current = Amperes = I
Time   = Seconds = t

THE FORMULA

$$Q = It$$

or   CHARGE = CURRENT × TIME
or   COULOMBS = AMPERES × SECONDS

Problems

■ Problem 1

Two amperes have been flowing for three seconds. How many coulombs of charge have flowed?

Given: $I = 2$ amperes
 $t = 3$ seconds
 $Q = ?$

Basic formula: $Q = I\,t$
Transposing (not necessary)
Substitute and solve: $Q = 2 \times 3$
 $Q = 6$ coulombs

■ Problem 2

Twenty coulombs of charge flow in a current of 4 amperes. How many seconds did it take for the charge to flow?

Given: $I = 4$ amperes
 $t = ?$
 $Q = 20$ coulombs

Basic formula: $Q = I\,t$

Transposing: $\dfrac{Q}{I} = \dfrac{\not{I}\,t}{\not{I}}$ *or* $\dfrac{Q}{I} = t$

Substitute and solve: $t = \dfrac{20}{4}$ *or* $t = 5$ seconds

■ Problem 3

It takes 2 seconds for 10 coulombs to flow, how many amperes of current are flowing?

Given: $I = ?$
 $t = 2$ seconds
 $Q = 10$ coulombs

Basic formula: $Q = I\,t$

Transposing: $\dfrac{Q}{t} = \dfrac{I\,\not{t}}{\not{t}}$ *or* $I = \dfrac{Q}{t}$

Substitute and solve: $I = \dfrac{10}{2}$ *or* $I = 5$ amperes

Current, then, depends upon the size of the charge and the number of seconds the charge flows.

REMEMBER

Current is the rate of electron flow.

Coulombs simply represent the amount of charge or the *quantity* of electrons. Current considers not only the quantity of electrons but also the period of time it takes for those electrons to flow.

1 coulomb = 6.28×10^{18} electrons, or 6,280,000,000,000,000,000 electrons.
1 ampere = 1 coulomb *per second.*

JOULES AND WORK

In electricity *work* is measured in *joules.*

THE FORMULA

$$W = VQ$$

W = work in joules
V = potential in volts
Q = charge in coulombs

Problems

■ Problem 1

How much work is expended in moving 5 coulombs through 2 volts of potential?

Given: V = 2 volts
Q = 5 coulombs
W = ?

Basic formula: W = V Q

Transposing (not necessary)

Substitute and solve: W = 2 × 5
W = 10 joules

■ Problem 2

20 joules of work have been expended to move a charge of 2 coulombs. How many volts were required to get the job done?

Given: V = ?
Q = 2 coulombs
W = 20 joules

Basic formula: W = V Q

Transposing: $\dfrac{W}{Q} = \dfrac{V\cancel{Q}}{\cancel{Q}}$ or $V = \dfrac{W}{Q}$

Substitute and solve: $\dfrac{20}{2} = 10$ volts

56

■ Problem 3

40 joules of work and 20 volts were required to move a certain charge. How large was the charge?

Given: $V = 20$ volts
$\qquad$ $Q = ?$
$\qquad$ $W = 40$ joules

Basic formula: $W = VQ$

Transposing: $\dfrac{W}{V} = \dfrac{\not{V}Q}{\not{V}}$ *or* $Q = \dfrac{W}{V}$

Substitute and solve: $\dfrac{40}{20} = 2$ coulombs

REMEMBER

When a charge is moved, work is done.

Any time a quantity of electrons is moved from one place to another work must be done, just as it requires work to move a pile of bricks from a truck to a house. If one powerful man (the force) is moving the bricks, he can move more bricks than several children (smaller forces).

Voltage is a force. A large voltage can move more electrons (charged particles) than several smaller voltages may move. But regardless of the size of voltage, it does work any time it moves electrons, and the amount of electrons moved will depend upon the size of the voltage moving them.

Electrical work depends upon the size of charge and the voltage moving the charge. This is the same as saying:

$$\text{Joules} = \text{Volts times Coulombs}$$
or $\text{Work} = \text{Voltage} \times \text{Charge}$
or $W = VQ$

POWER

In electricity *power* is measured in *watts*. (Power represents a force pushing a charge at a certain *rate*.)

THE FORMULA

$W = EI$ or $P = EI$

$P =$ wattage in watts
$E =$ voltage in volts
$I =$ amperage in amperes

Problems

■ Problem 1

How much power (wattage) is being used by an electric heater that draws 10 amperes at a pressure of 100 volts?

Given: E = 100   volts
         I = 10   amperes
         P = ?

Basic formula: $P = EI$

Transposing (not necessary)

Substitute and solve: $P = 100 \times 10$ *or*   P = 1000 watts

■ Problem 2

How much voltage is present if 50 watts are used while 5 amperes are being pushed through an electrical appliance?

This is the same as asking how much voltage is present if 50 watts of power are used while 5 coulombs of electrons are being pushed through a conductor in 1 second.

Given: E = ?
        I = 5
       W = 50

Basic formula: $P = EI$

Transposing: $\dfrac{P}{I} = \dfrac{E\cancel{I}}{\cancel{I}}$ *or* $E = \dfrac{P}{I}$

Substitute and solve: $\dfrac{50}{5} = 10$ volts

■ Problem 3

An appliance rated at 100 watts and 20 volts will have how many amperes flowing when it is used at its rated power?

Given: E = 20   volts
        I = ?
       W = 100   watts

Basic formula: $P = EI$

Transposing: $\dfrac{P}{E} = \dfrac{\cancel{E}I}{\cancel{E}}$ *or* $I = \dfrac{P}{E}$

Substitute and solve: $\dfrac{100}{20} = 5$ amperes

Work depends upon *voltage* and *charge*. This is the same as saying that work depends upon volts and coulombs.

Power depends upon work accomplished in a certain period of time. This is the same as saying that power depends upon voltage times amperage, because amperage represents coulombs *per second*. Any time one thinks in terms of something per second he is thinking of *rate,* and, as stated above, *power is the rate of doing work.*

$$\text{Power} = \text{Volts times Amperes}$$
$$or \quad \text{Watts} = \text{Volts} \quad \times \quad \text{Amperes}$$
$$or \quad \text{W} = \text{E I}$$

SUMMARY

Two Important Formulas

The two formulas you will use the most deal with:

REMEMBER

Ohm's Law: $E = I R$
Power: $P = E I$

You now know how to use both of these formulas. It is well that you thoroughly familiarize yourself with every application given on the preceding pages, and that you work all of the practice problems at the end of this chapter. You will need to take advantage of every opportunity in order to learn completely the use of these two very important helpmates.

You will sometimes find problems dealing with electrical applications for which you do not have a formula handy. If you have a good background in algebra, the two formulas above can be "manipulated" to serve many applications. However, if your background in algebra is limited, you can use *both* formulas to arrive at *one* answer. Although this procedure will take a bit more time than the manipulation of any one formula, the results are every bit as accurate.

Here is an example:

Assume you have an electric motor which requires 125 volts for proper operation. Further assume it has a resistance of $62\frac{1}{2}$ ohms when running. You need to know how much wattage this motor will consume.

How will you work the problem if your background in algebra has been limited?

From having read the problem you know you must find wattage. Wattage is *power* so it follows you will need to use the power formula.

$$P = E I$$

You begin by setting down the information in standard procedure:

Given: E = 125 volts
          R = 62.5 ohms
          W = ?

Basic formula:

Here you get stuck! You cannot possibly use the formula as it is stated because you lack one very essential piece of information. You lack amperage — *I*.

Yet you know you must somehow use the formula in order to secure the answer. What can you do?

Take another look at the information given: *voltage* and *resistance*. With voltage and resistance given you can use the Ohm's Law formula to determine the amperage.

$$E = I R \quad or \quad I = \frac{E}{R} \qquad so: \quad I = \frac{125}{62.5} = 2 \text{ amperes}$$

You can now use your *power formula*. You have all the necessary "known" values.

$$P = E I \qquad so: \quad P = 125 \times 2 = 250 \text{ watts}$$

Your problem is solved. True, you had to use *two* formulas to secure the desired result, but you *do* have the answer and it is correct.

Carry the problem a step further. You know the motor will consume 250 watts, but how much does this represent in *horsepower*? If you have learned your lessons well to this point you know 1 horsepower is equal to 746 watts, so:

$$746 \overline{\smash{)}250.00} \quad .33$$

The answer, .33, is equivalent to ⅓ horsepower.

It is important to remember this problem. You will have to use variations of it many times in the future.

REVIEW QUESTIONS

1. A 6-volt battery is hooked in series with a 3-ohm resistance. How much current will flow?

2. A light bulb having a 300-ohm resistance when lighted, draws a current of .5 ampere. How much voltage will be required to light the bulb at normal brilliance?

3. A 12-volt automobile radio has an operating resistance of 4 ohms. Under normal conditions, will a 6-ampere fuse burn out if placed in series with the radio switch?

4. A toaster is rated at 115 volts and 10 amperes. How much wattage will it consume?

5. A flashlight is rated at 3 volts. It consumes .45 watt. What is the amperage of the bulb?

6. A 1-horsepower motor is rated at 3.73 amperes. What voltage must be supplied to this motor to have it function properly?

7. An appliance has a resistance of 500 ohms, and a rated wattage of 100. How much wattage will it consume?

8. From the formula $E = IR$ one can determine that as resistance gets larger, current flow becomes less. On the other hand, as voltage becomes greater, current flow becomes _____.

9. Using the formula $E = IR$ one can see that as I becomes greater and resistance remains the same, E must become _____.

10. Using the formula $E = IR$ one can see that as R gets larger, and I remains the same, E must become _____.

11. Using the formula $E = IR$ one can see that as E becomes larger and I remains the same, R must have become _____.

12. Using the formula $E = IR$ one can see that as R becomes less and E remains the same, I becomes _____.

13. Using the formula $E = IR$ one can see that as I becomes less and E remains the same, R must have become _____.

14. Using the formula $E = IR$ one can see that as E becomes less and I remains the same, R must have become _____.

15. Using the formula $W = EI$ one can see that as wattage becomes greater and voltage remains the same, I must become _____.

16. A nichrome wire draws 5 amperes from a 120-volt line. The wattage consumed is 600 watts. Answer the following questions:
    a) What is the resistance?
    b) If an extra length of nichrome wire is added to the above piece, the total resistance is increased to 50 ohms. If the voltage remains the same, will the amperage be more or less?
    c) Referring to b above, will the wattage be more or less?
    d) Will the nichrome wire heat more or less with the extra 50 ohms' resistance?

17. A light bulb having a tungsten filament has a certain resistance:
    a) Will that resistance become more or less as the filament heats?
    b) Will the light bulb pass more or less current as the filament heats?
    c) Will the light bulb consume more or less wattage as the filament heats?

18. A certain piece of wire has a resistance of 2 ohms. Another wire of exactly the same length, but twice the cross-sectional area will have a resistance of (a) four times as great, (b) twice as great, (c) one half as much, (d) one fourth as much.

19. A piece of No. 22 copper wire 1 foot long has a specific resistance. The resistance of a piece of No. 22 copper wire 2 feet long will have a resistance of (a) twice as much, (b) four times as much, (c) one half as much, (d) one fourth as much?

20. According to Ohm's Law it takes 4 volts to push _____ amperes through 2 ohms of resistance.

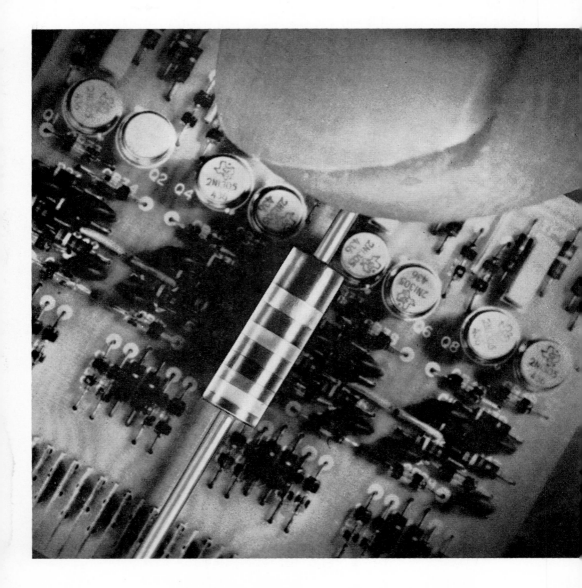

Unit 7

SERIES AND PARALLEL CIRCUITRY

When any two or more electrical devices are wired in *series* the same current which flows through any one of the devices will flow through all.

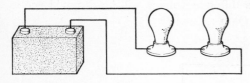

This is a pictorial diagram of a simple series connection.

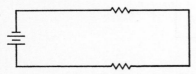

This is a schematic diagram of the above circuit.

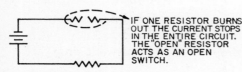

IF ONE RESISTOR BURNS OUT THE CURRENT STOPS IN THE ENTIRE CIRCUIT. THE "OPEN" RESISTOR ACTS AS AN OPEN SWITCH.

Examine this circuit carefully. What will happen if one resistor (lamp) burns out?

From the above one can see that the *same* current which flows through one resistor must also flow through the other. Not only does the same current flow through both, but the same *amount* will flow through both resistors.

You will recall from Ohm's Law the higher the resistance the lower will be the current flow if the voltage is held constant. In a series circuit, *less* current will get through the entire circuit than will get through the highest resistance in the hookup, but once the total resistance is added up and the current is determined, the same amount of current will flow through the entire circuit. As each resistance is added into the circuit the circuit amperage becomes less.

Note the effect of the different resistances in these two circuits.

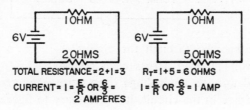

TOTAL RESISTANCE = 2 + 1 = 3

CURRENT = $I = \frac{E}{R}$ OR $\frac{6}{3}$ = 2 AMPERES

$R_T = 1 + 5 = 6$ OHMS

$I = \frac{E}{R}$ OR $\frac{6}{6}$ = 1 AMP

63

In the above example two things happened:

1. Placing a larger resistance in series with the battery *added* to a larger total resistance.
2. Placing the larger resistor in series *cut down* the flow of current.

THE RULE

Resistors in series ADD.

Voltage Drop in Series

If the same amount of current flows through each resistor in the series circuit, and if each resistor is a different value, a different voltage will be dropped across each resistor. This can be proved with Ohm's Law:

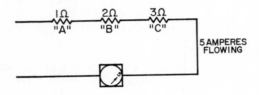

Resistor A

  E = I R

  E = 5 × 1

   = 5-volt drop

Resistor B

  E = I R

  E = 5 × 2

   = 10-volt drop

Resistor C

  E = I R

  E = 5 × 3

   = 15-volt drop

Adding the three voltage drops yields a *total* voltage of 30 volts (5 + 10 + 15). If a total of 30 volts have been dropped across all three resistors it must follow that 30 volts is the source voltage. True, a very small resistance is found in the wires connecting the resistors, in the ammeter, and even in the voltage source itself, but these are so small they are not considered.

The preceding voltage drop problem could have been approached another way. Given the schematic diagram below with its associated values, answer the questions involved:

1. What is the amperage through the circuit?
2. What is the voltage drop across each resistor?

Before one can determine the voltage drop across any resistor, or before one can determine amperage in the circuit, it is necessary to figure the total resistance.

Finding Total Resistance

To determine the total resistance in a *series circuit* is a simple matter — *add* all the resistances.

$$1 \text{ ohm} + 2 \text{ ohms} + 3 \text{ ohms} = 6 \text{ ohms}$$

REMEMBER

Resistors in series ADD.

Determining the Amperage

To determine the amperage through *all* the resistors (which is the same as through each one), use Ohm's Law:

$$I = \frac{E}{R} = \frac{30}{6} = 5 \text{ amperes}$$

THE RULE

Amperage in one part of a SERIES CIRCUIT is the same as in any other part of the circuit.

Voltage Drop

Now that the resistance of each resistor is known, and the amperage through each is also known, the voltage drops may be determined by using Ohm's Law for each resistor. This would be accomplished as shown on page 64.

$$E = I R$$

REMEMBER

The sum of the voltage dropped across ALL resistors must equal the source voltage.

Some Important Principles

From working with this network you have learned several very important principles which *always* apply to series circuits:

1. The amperage is the same throughout the entire series circuit.
2. Resistance in a series circuit always *adds*. The total resistance is the *sum* of all the individual resistors.
3. A specific voltage will be dropped across *each* resistor.
4. The sum of all voltage drops will equal the source voltage.
5. If any part of a series circuit becomes "open" the entire circuit goes dead.

Learn the above five points well. They represent a large share of the frame-work upon which electrical circuitry is built, and they will be used time and time again!

Summary Problems for Series Circuits

Given:

Find:

1. What is the amperage through each resistor?
2. What is the voltage drop across each resistor?
3. What is the total voltage drop?

Solutions:

A. Before one can determine the amperage through the resistors, and before voltage drop can be determined, the total resistance of the circuit must be found.

$$1 \text{ ohm} + 2 \text{ ohms} + 4 \text{ ohms} + 5 \text{ ohms} = 12 \text{ ohms}$$

REMEMBER

Resistances in series add.

B. The amperage through each resistor may now be calculated by using Ohm's Law.

$$E = I R$$

Transpose letters and solve:

$$I = \frac{E}{R}$$

$$I = \frac{24 \text{ volts}}{12 \text{ ohms}}$$

$I = 2$ amperes through *each* resistor and through the entire circuit. Amperage remains the same throughout a series circuit.

C. Determine individual voltage drops, using Ohm's Law.

$$E = I R$$

Resistor *A* E = 2 amperes × 1 ohm = 2-volt drop
         B E = 2 amperes × 2 ohms = 4-volt drop
         C E = 2 amperes × 4 ohms = 8-volt drop
         D E = 2 amperes × 5 ohms = 10-volt drop

D. Add all voltage drops to determine the voltage source = 24 volts.

Computing Wattage in a Series Circuit

Wattage represents electrical *power*. It also represents *heat loss* because the power consumed by a resistor changes to heat within that resistor. Many of the electrical appliances in home and industry depend upon this factor: flat irons, electric ranges, waffle irons, toasters, electric heaters, and innumerable everyday electrical apparatus.

It is simple to calculate wattage in a series circuit. All one needs to know is the total resistance and the amperage — then apply the formula.

THE FORMULA

$$P = I^2 R$$

Something New

Hold on! Here is something new. What does I^2 mean? It is nothing to fear. It simply means:

$$I \times I$$

What are some other examples?

$$4^2 = 4 \times 4$$
$$8^2 = 8 \times 8$$
$$I^2 = I \times I$$

The small ^{2} in I^2 is called a *power number*. It tells one how many times a number is multiplied times itself. 2^2 is the same as saying 2×2. 2^3 (2 to the third power) means $2 \times 2 \times 2$. 2^5 means 2 to the fifth power, or $2 \times 2 \times 2 \times 2 \times 2$.

It is a sort of mathematical shorthand. Imagine how much simpler it is to write 10^{18} (10 to the eighteenth power) than it is to write $10 \times 10 \times 10 \times 10 \times 10 \times 10 \times 10 \times 10 \times 10 \times 10 \times 10 \times 10 \times 10 \times 10 \times 10 \times 10 \times 10 \times 10$. Or, to put it another way, 10^{18} means "1" followed by 18 zeros (ciphers).

Can you now better understand what is meant when one says one coulomb is equal to 6.28×10^{18} electrons? How much simpler this is than writing 6,280,000,000,000,000,000!

But Where Does I^2 Come From?

"But," you might say, "where does the I^2 come from in the first place? Does this have a relationship to Ohm's Law?"

It certainly has!

Go back a unit for just a moment.

What was the *basic* formula for power?

Of course, $P = E\,I$.

And, what does the *E* in that formula stand for?

It comes from Ohm's Law: $E = IR$.

Well, then, put all of this information together:

If $P = EI$ it is the same as saying $P = (I \times R) \times I$, and this is the same as saying $P = I \times I \times R$. But, why write $I \times I$ when I^2 means the same thing and can be stated in shorter terms? The formula then becomes:

$P = I^2R$ which means the same as $P = I \times I \times R$, or the same as $P = (I \times R) \times I$, or the same as $P = EI$.

Fitting All of the Information Together

How does all this information fit together? Assume you have the following problem:

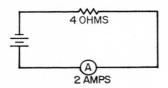

What is the *power* consumed by this circuit?

First, what is the *new* formula?

$$P = I^2 R$$

Substitute and solve:

$$P = 2 \times 2 \times 4$$
$$P = 16 \text{ watts}$$

Some Important Questions

Could the problem have been solved if the *new* power formula had not been known? Yes! the two *old* formulas could have been used:

$$E = IR$$
$$\text{and} \quad P = EI$$

Why use *both* formulas? Because, in the original problem voltage was *not* given. Hence, one could not simply have used the old power formula, $P = EI$. It would have first been necessary to solve for *E* by using the formula, $E = IR$. *Then,* and only then, could the old power formula have been used. How much easier it was to use the new formula, even though the two old standbys could have worked!

THE FORMULA
$P = I^2 R$

One More Problem

Try one more problem to make certain you have the idea straight.

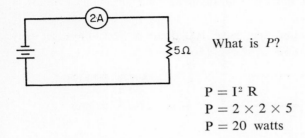

What is *P*?

$$P = I^2 R$$
$$P = 2 \times 2 \times 5$$
$$P = 20 \text{ watts}$$

Wattage Rating of Resistors

When one is designing electronic circuits, it is often necessary to determine the *ohms* rating a resistor should have in order to control or limit the current. Something else is important, too!

One must *also* secure a resistor *large* enough in physical size that it will not burn out when placed in the circuit.

What does this mean?

It means that the power used in any resistor *changes to heat* within that resistor and is lost to the surrounding air. This heat loss is called the I^2R loss — the watts or power loss. If the resistor is not large enough in physical size, it will not be able to dissipate enough heat and it will burn up. What determines the physical size?

In large part the wattage rating determines the physical size. Sound like double talk? It is not.

Take a typical example. Assume you have the following circuit:

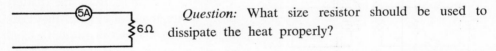

Question: What size resistor should be used to dissipate the heat properly?

Right here you might guess wrongly and say, "The size has already been determined. It is 6 ohms." *But,* this is *not* the size referred to. When one mentions resistor size in connection with heat dissipation he is referring to the proper *wattage* rating, not the resistance rating.

Now back to the problem: What size resistor should be used?

To determine this one may use the new power (wattage) formula:

$$P = I^2 R$$
$$\text{so:} \quad P = 5 \times 5 \times 6$$
$$P = 150 \text{ watts}$$

Summing up, then, it will take a 6-ohm, 150-watt resistor to get the job done.

Remember: The physical size of a resistor has nothing whatever to do with its ohms rating.

A 1,000,000-ohm resistor (1 megohm) may be exactly the same physical size as a 100-ohm resistor. On the other hand it may be smaller *or* larger. The physical size determines how much heat it will dissipate, *not* how many ohms it represents.

All of the resistors shown below may have 100 ohms of resistance, yet they vary considerably in wattage rating.

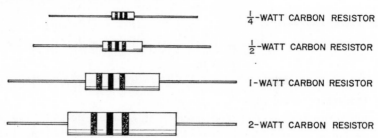

$\frac{1}{4}$-WATT CARBON RESISTOR

$\frac{1}{2}$-WATT CARBON RESISTOR

1-WATT CARBON RESISTOR

2-WATT CARBON RESISTOR

PARALLEL CIRCUITRY

A parallel circuit is one in which two or more branch circuits are provided through which current may flow.

A parallel circuit differs from a series circuit in that *voltage remains the same* throughout the circuit, but amperage may vary considerably. This is the exact opposite of a series circuit.

Compare:

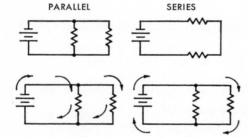

PARALLEL   SERIES

Examine the parallel circuit closely.

Electrons coming from the battery have more than one path they can follow. Since the two resistors are connected in parallel, or "branched," the electrons can follow either one or both paths.

Because the electrons may take *two* paths, providing neither resistor is "open," the *total* resistance is *less* than it would be if the resistors were hooked in series.

THE RULE

In a parallel circuit the TOTAL resistance is ALWAYS LESS than the smallest resistor in the circuit.

How can this be possible?

An analogy will help clarify the point.

Imagine a roadway just wide enough for one lane of cars. At a set speed, only a certain number of cars will be able to flow. One could say, then, the road has a certain resistance to the flow of traffic.

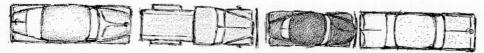

Would it be possible to increase the flow of traffic? One way to increase traffic flow could be accomplished by speeding the cars. But, assume they are already going as fast as they can. How else might the traffic flow be increased?

Traffic could be doubled by opening a new roadway . . . set up a "branch" road so the two lanes would be in parallel.

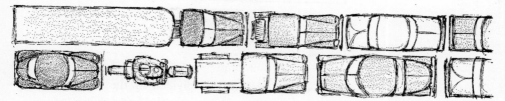

Even though each lane would still have a certain amount of resistance to the flow of traffic, twice as many cars would get through. This means the *total* resistance would be less than both "resistors." The resistance would be one-half as great as the resistance of the single lane.

Electrical resistances are very much like the roadway. The more branch circuits there are, the less will be the total resistance, because more paths are being provided over which the total electrons will be able to flow. With a lowering of resistance naturally comes an *increase* in amperage if voltage is held constant.

In a *series* circuit the job of finding the total resistance is a simple matter; one needs only to add all of the resistors. Figuring the total resistance in a parallel circuit is not this simple. There are many methods for calculating resistance in a parallel circuit. Several of these will be carefully studied.

Calculating Parallel Resistance

Method 1

The simplest method for determining parallel resistance can be used providing all the resistors are of equal value.

Use the following circuit as an example:

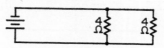

Since *both* resistors in this circuit have 4 ohms each, one may simply divide the 4 ohms by the number of resistors — 2.

71

$$R = \frac{4}{2}$$

$$R_t = 2 \text{ ohms}$$

Try another:

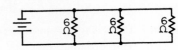

$$R_t = \frac{6}{3}$$

$$R_t = 2 \text{ ohms}$$

One more:

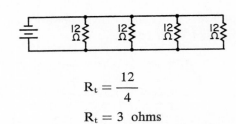

$$R_t = \frac{12}{4}$$

$$R_t = 3 \text{ ohms}$$

In method 1 the resistance of *one* resistor was divided by the *number* of resistors. This method works *only* when all resistors have the same value.

In method 2, there will be two resistors, but each will have a *different* value.

Method 2

In this method there are *two* resistors but *each* has a *different value* of resistance. Thus:

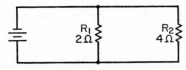

Use this formula: $R_t = \dfrac{R_1 \times R_2}{R_1 + R_2}$

Substitute and solve: $R_t = \dfrac{2 \times 4}{2 + 4} = \dfrac{8}{6}$

$$R_t = 1.333 \text{ ohms}$$

One more:

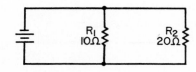

Formula: $R_t = \dfrac{R_1 \times R_2}{R_1 + R_2}$

Substitute and solve: $\quad R_t = \dfrac{10 \times 20}{10 + 20} = \dfrac{200}{30}$

$$R_t = 6.667 \text{ ohms}$$

Method 3

This method will work for *any number* of resistors having *any value* of resistance. It involves a formula which should be memorized and used often. Thus:

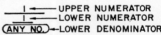

Use this formula: $\quad R_t = \dfrac{1}{\dfrac{1}{R_1} + \dfrac{1}{R_2} + \dfrac{1}{R_3} + \text{etc., etc.}}$

Substitute and solve: $\quad R_t = \dfrac{1}{\dfrac{1}{60} + \dfrac{1}{200} + \dfrac{1}{300}}$

$$= \dfrac{1}{.0167 + .005 + .0033} = \dfrac{1}{.0250}$$

$$= 40 \text{ ohms}$$

Points to Remember

Whenever one has a problem in the form shown below, a "reciprocal" mathematics problem is being solved. To solve it, one simply takes the lower denominator and divides it into the lower numerator. That answer is then divided into the upper numerator.

$$\dfrac{1 \leftarrow \text{UPPER NUMERATOR}}{\underline{1 \leftarrow \text{LOWER NUMERATOR}}}$$
$$\text{(ANY NO.)} \leftarrow \text{LOWER DENOMINATOR}$$

Try Another, Completely Worked Out

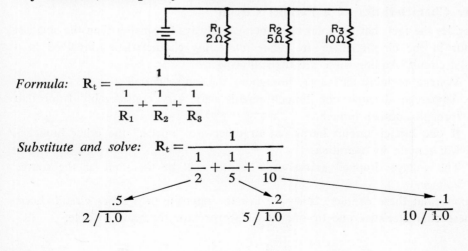

Formula: $\quad R_t = \dfrac{1}{\dfrac{1}{R_1} + \dfrac{1}{R_2} + \dfrac{1}{R_3}}$

Substitute and solve: $\quad R_t = \dfrac{1}{\dfrac{1}{2} + \dfrac{1}{5} + \dfrac{1}{10}}$

$$.5 \quad 2\overline{)1.0} \qquad .2 \quad 5\overline{)1.0} \qquad .1 \quad 10\overline{)1.0}$$

Add: $.5 + .2 + .1 = .8$

$$R_t = \frac{1}{.8} \qquad or \qquad .8\overline{\smash{\big)}1.000}^{\,1.25}$$

$$R_t = 1.25 \text{ ohms (total resistance)}$$

Work One More Problem

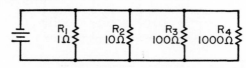

Formula: $\quad R_t = \dfrac{1}{\dfrac{1}{R_1} + \dfrac{1}{R_2} + \dfrac{1}{R_3} + \dfrac{1}{R_4}}$

Substitute and solve: $\quad R_t = \dfrac{1}{\dfrac{1}{1} + \dfrac{1}{10} + \dfrac{1}{100} + \dfrac{1}{1000}}$

$$= \frac{1}{1.00 + .10 + .01 + .001}$$

$$= \frac{1}{1.111}$$

$$= .9 \text{ ohm (total resistance)}$$

NOTE: In each of these resistance problems the *total* resistance *always* was *less* than the smallest resistance in the network!

Other Characteristics of a Parallel Circuit

Besides the fact that the total resistance will always be smaller than the smallest resistor in the circuit, there are other interesting characteristics involved in a parallel circuit. Among these are the following:

1. Voltage remains the same throughout the entire circuit.
2. Amperage through one branch circuit may vary considerably from that through another branch.
3. If one branch circuit burns out or otherwise "opens," the other branches will remain in operation.
4. The voltage dropped across *each* resistor will be the same as the source voltage.

Notice that these characteristics are just the opposite of a series circuit. Look at these characteristics one by one and discover how they are possible.

Voltage Remains the Same

This needs little explanation. If one looks at a schematic diagram of a parallel

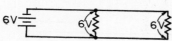

circuit it is obvious the source voltage is impressed *directly across* each resistor. Thus, the same voltage is impressed — and dropped — across each parallel resistor, regardless of its resistance.

Amperage May Vary

If one thinks about Ohm's Law it should be obvious that amperage may vary from one branch circuit to the next, depending upon the resistance and voltage involved.

Take an example:

Since the same voltage is impressed across *each resistor,* and since one knows the value of each resistor, it is a simple matter to substitute in Ohm's Law.

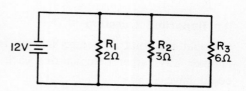

Amperage Through Resistor R_1
Basic formula: $E = I R$

Transpose: $I = \dfrac{E}{R}$

Substitute and solve: $I = \dfrac{12}{2} = 6$ amperes

Amperage Through Resistor R_2
Basic formula: $E = I R$

Transpose: $I = \dfrac{E}{R}$

Substitute and solve: $I = \dfrac{12}{3} = 4$ amperes

Amperage Through Resistor R_3
Basic formula: $E = I R$

Transpose: $I = \dfrac{E}{R}$

Substitute and solve: $I = \dfrac{12}{6} = 2$ amperes

You now have the amperage flowing through *each* resistor. You also know the amperage varied through each. Can you now determine the *total* amperage flowing *from the battery?*

To compute this simply add all the amperages.

6 amperes + 4 amperes + 2 amperes = 12 amperes

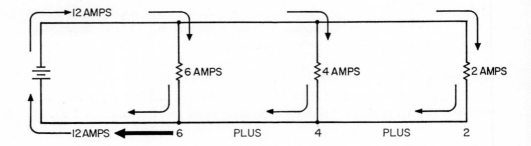

An Important Question

Could the total amperage flowing from the battery have been determined in another way rather than figuring each resistor's amperage individually? It surely could have.

By calculating the *total* resistance of the *parallel* circuit the amperage flow from the battery could have been calculated. Thus:

$$R_t = \cfrac{1}{\cfrac{1}{R_1} + \cfrac{1}{R_2} + \cfrac{1}{R_3}}$$

$$= \cfrac{1}{\cfrac{1}{2} + \cfrac{1}{3} + \cfrac{1}{6}}$$

$$= \cfrac{1}{.5 + .333 + .167}$$

$$= \cfrac{1}{1.000} = 1 \text{ ohm}$$

Then calculate the total amperes flowing from the battery.

Basic formula: $\quad E = I R$

Transpose: $\quad I = \dfrac{E}{R}$

Substitute and solve: $\quad I = \dfrac{12 \text{ volts}}{1 \text{ ohm}} = 12 \text{ amperes}$

You can see the amperage total was the same regardless of the method used to compute it. This is as it should be. If a difference had existed, it would have indicated an error in computation.

An Open Branch

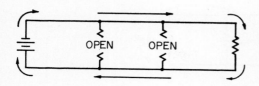

If one or more branch resistors (circuits) are open, amperage will continue to flow through the remaining resistors. Naturally the *total* amperage would become less for each resistor which would be open.

Summary of the Principles of a Parallel Circuit

Voltage remains the same throughout a parallel circuit.

Amperage through different branch circuits may vary.

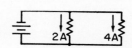

If one branch circuit burns out, the other branch or branches will remain in operation.

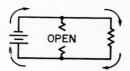

SERIES-PARALLEL CIRCUITS

All circuits are not simply series *or* parallel. Many circuits contain *both* within one.

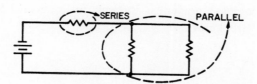

The above circuit has *one* resistor *in series* and *two parallel* resistors. It will have the characteristics of *both* series and parallel circuits. To understand its operation fully, we will have to break it down into individual circuits, and finally relate the individuals to one another.

Total Resistance

What is the *total* resistance of the circuit? Since it contains both series and parallel resistors, it will be necessary to use more than one method for solving for total resistance. As stated above, one of the best ways to accomplish this is to break the circuit down into individual circuits.

Thus:

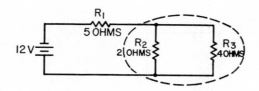

First, figure the resistance of resistors R_2 and R_3. Since they are in parallel you can use one of the resistance formulas.

$$R_t = \frac{R_1 \times R_2}{R_1 + R_2}$$

$$= \frac{2 \times 4}{2 + 4} = \frac{8}{6}$$

$$= 1.333 \text{ ohms}$$

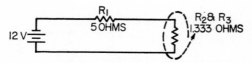

This is just the same as having *one* resistor of 1.333 ohms in series with resistor R_1. If the circuit were re-drawn, it would look like this:

Second, calculating the *total* resistance is a simple matter because the resistors are now in series. All one need do is *add.*

$$R_1 + R_2 \text{ and } R_3$$

or   5 ohms + 1.333 = 6.333 ohms (total resistance)

Calculating Amperage

One may now compute amperage through the network. Source voltage and the *total* resistance are known.

Basic formula: $E = I R$

Transpose: $I = \dfrac{E}{R}$

Substitute and solve: $I = \dfrac{12 \text{ volts}}{6.333 \text{ ohms}} = 1.9$ amperes

Thus, 1.9 amperes represent the current leaving the 12-volt battery, and it also represents the amperage going *through* the series resistor R_1. But, 1.9 amperes will *not* go through R_2 and R_3 individually, because both are in parallel and have different resistances. However, 1.9 amperes are *available* to both and will be divided between them in ratio to their resistances. *Remember:* Amperage through a parallel circuit may vary in the different branches.

What will be the amperage through R_2 and R_3?

Many methods could be used to calculate amperage through these resistors.

The following method will perhaps provide more understanding than some other.

Because R_1 is in *series* with the two parallel resistors R_2 and R_3, it necessarily follows that a definite *voltage drop* will occur across R_1. Remember: *A specific amount of voltage is always dropped across each resistor in a series circuit.* This voltage drop can be calculated using Ohm's Law.

Basic formula: $E = IR$

Substitute and solve: $E = 1.9$ amperes $\times$ 5 ohms $= 9.5$ volts dropped

This means only 2.5 volts $(12 - 9.5)$ will be available for R_2 and R_3, and since they are in *parallel*, the full 2.5 volts will be impressed across each.

Since the available voltage is known, and the resistance of each parallel resistor is also known, amperage through each may be determined by using Ohm's Law:

<table>
<tr><td>**Resistor R_2**</td><td>**Resistor R_3**</td></tr>
<tr><td>$I = \dfrac{E}{R}$</td><td>$I = \dfrac{E}{R}$</td></tr>
<tr><td>$= \dfrac{2.5 \text{ volts}}{2 \text{ ohms}}$</td><td>$= \dfrac{2.5 \text{ volts}}{4 \text{ ohms}}$</td></tr>
<tr><td>$= 1.25$ amperes</td><td>$= .625$ amperes</td></tr>
</table>

To prove the answers, one may add the amperage through R_2 and R_3:

$$1.25 + .625 = 1.875 \text{ amperes}$$

The total is *very* close to the 1.9 amperes originally passing through R_1. Hence, the answers check out.

Why did the two amperages not add *exactly* to 1.9 amperes? Remember, when the total resistance of the two parallel resistors R_2 and R_3 was calculated, the figure was carried out three decimal places (to 1.333). Had it been possible to carry the decimal fraction out to infinity the two amperages would have totaled, *exactly*, 1.9 amperes.

Summary of Series-Parallel Circuits

Series-parallel circuits take on the characteristics of *both* series and parallel networks.

I. Figure the Total Resistance

A. Break the circuit down. In this circuit it would be easiest to figure first the total resistance of parallel resistors *D, E,* and *F*. Use formula

$$R_t = \cfrac{1}{\cfrac{1}{R_D} + \cfrac{1}{R_E} + \cfrac{1}{R_F}}$$

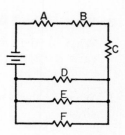

B. Redraw the circuit.

C. Add the total series resistances.

A + B + C + D, E, and F

II. Calculate the Amperage From the Battery

Simply substitute in Ohm's Law.

$$I = \frac{E}{R} = \frac{\text{Battery Voltage}}{\text{Total Resistance } (A + B + C + D, E, \text{ and } F)}$$

III. Calculate the Amperage Through Each Individual Parallel Resistor

A. Figure the voltage drop across resistors *A, B, C.*

E = Amperes from battery × resistance of A + B + C

B. Subtract the voltage drop of series resistors *A, B, C* from the total source voltage. This will leave an *available remaining voltage.*

C. Use Ohm's Law to calculate amperage through each individual parallel resistor.

$$I = \frac{\text{Remaining Available Voltage}}{\text{Resistance of Resistor D}}$$

$$+ I = \frac{\text{Remaining Available Voltage}}{\text{Resistance of E}}$$

$$+ I = \frac{\text{Remaining Available Voltage}}{\text{Resistance of F}}$$

REVIEW QUESTIONS

1. *a)* What is the voltage of the battery?
   b) What is the voltage drop across the resistor?

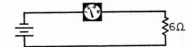

2. What is the current:
   a) at point *A*?
   b) at point *B*?
   c) at point *C*?

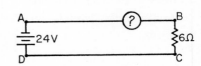

3. What is the total resistance?

4. What is the voltage drop across each resistor? (See question 3.)

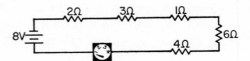

5. What is the wattage being consumed by this circuit?

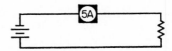

6. What is the wattage of this electric iron?

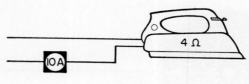
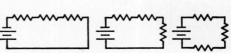

7. Which circuit is different?

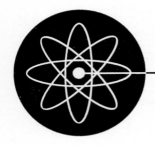

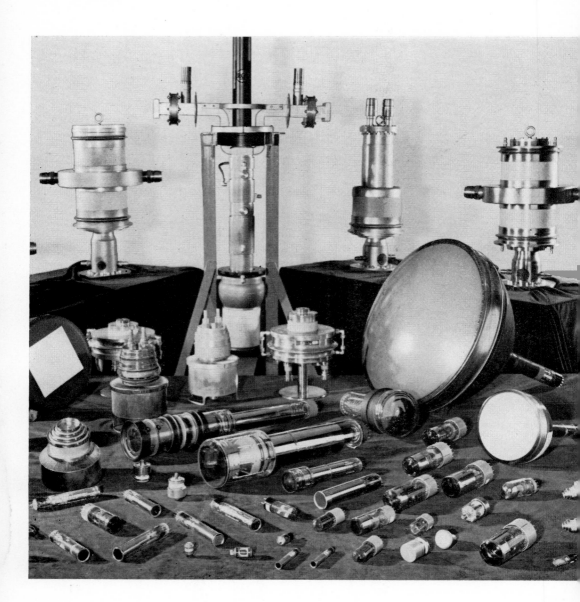

Unit 8

COMPONENTS, SWITCHES, AND CIRCUITS

In this unit considerable attention will be given to many different circuits and switching arrangements. Usually the novice electrician thinks of a switch as being a device for either turning a light on or off. In reality switches can do much more than this. By arranging them in circuits switches can do everything from turning a motor on or off, to operating the flip-flop circuit of an electronic computer.

If you are alert you will notice considerable repetition involved in this presentation. This is true because *all* the circuits presented, no matter how complex they seem to be, will simply be variations of the series, the parallel, or the series-parallel circuit.

It is quite impossible to understand even relatively simple wiring diagrams if one cannot "follow a schematic." No one — no matter how much technical information he may have memorized — can consider himself competent to design, troubleshoot, or service electrical apparatus unless he has a thorough and comprehensive understanding of circuitry.

This unit has been designed in a special way to evoke the greatest possible learning. So that you may anticipate a sequence of events a special format has been designed.

First, the components will be introduced along with their schematic symbols. If the component and symbol are used in *several* problems, they will be introduced in only the first two. Thereafter the *circuit* may be the first introduction to the problem.

Second, the circuit will be shown and if need be, introduced.

Third, problems will be introduced which bear directly upon the circuit. It is strongly recommended that the student attempt to work the problem before looking at the solution, which is involved in the next step.

Fourth, the problem will be answered and pertinent explanations given providing they lend clarity and understanding. In this unit you will use every major concept and principle learned thus far.

Circuit 1

Components

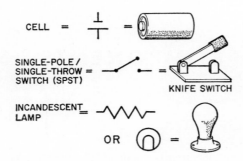

CELL =

SINGLE-POLE /
SINGLE-THROW =
SWITCH (SPST)

KNIFE SWITCH

INCANDESCENT =
LAMP

OR ⌒ =

Circuit

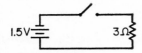

1.5V   3Ω

This is a series circuit. No current will flow until the switch is closed.

Problems

1. How much current will flow when the switch is closed?
2. How much voltage will be dropped across the resistor with the switch in the open position?
3. How much voltage will be dropped across the resistor with the switch in the closed position?
4. How much wattage is consumed by the resistor?
5. How "large" should the resistor be in order adequately to dissipate the heat developed, and prevent burnout of the resistor?

Answers

1. .5 ampere will flow with the switch closed. $I = \dfrac{E}{R}$
2. No voltage will be dropped across the resistor with the switch in the open position. *A voltage drop never occurs unless current flows.*
3. 1.5 volts will be dropped across the resistor. $E = I\,R$
4. .75 watt will be consumed. $P = E\,I$ *or* $P = I^2 R$
5. It should be at least .75 watt in size. (See above.) It may, however, be any size larger.

Circuit 2
Components

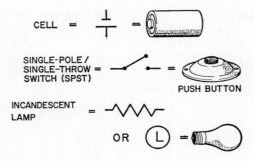

CELL =

SINGLE-POLE /
SINGLE-THROW =
SWITCH (SPST)

PUSH BUTTON

INCANDESCENT
LAMP =

OR L =

Circuit

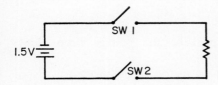

SW 1

1.5V

SW 2

This is a circuit having two single-pole/ single-throw switches in series with a cell and resistor, such as an incandescent lamp.

Problems

1. How much current will flow with switch Sw_1 closed?
2. How much current will flow with *both* switches closed?
3. What will be the voltage drop across the resistor?

Answers

1. *No* current will flow unless *both* switches are closed.
   An opening in any part of a series circuit will cause the entire circuit to go dead.
2. The only information given is the voltage of the cell. This is not enough. Unless one had an ammeter to insert in series with the line, it would not be possible to calculate amperage without knowing the value of the resistor.
3. Even though amperage is not given, one knows the full 1.5 volts of the battery will be dropped across the resistor. Why? Because it is the only resistor in the circuit. If two or more resistors were present, one would not dare make this statement.

Circuit 3
Components

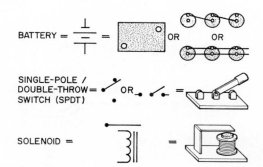

BATTERY =

SINGLE-POLE /
DOUBLE-THROW =
SWITCH (SPDT)

SOLENOID =

Circuit

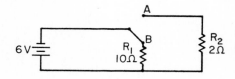

6 V

A

B

R₁
10Ω

R₂
2Ω

This is a double series circuit. It is *not* a parallel circuit since the switch can be in only *one* position at one time.

Solenoids are the resistors.

Problems

1. With the switch in position *B*, what will be the voltage drop across resistor R_2?
2. With the switch in position *A*, what will be the current flow?
3. With the switch in position *B*, how much power will the circuit consume?

Answers

1. This is a catch question. With the switch in position *B*, there is no voltage drop across R_2 because it has no current through it.
2. With the switch in position *A*, 3 amperes of current will flow.

$$I = \frac{E}{R}$$

3. With the switch in position *B*, 3.6 watts will be consumed. To solve this problem, *first* find the amperage through R_1:

$$I = \frac{E}{R} = \frac{6}{10} = .6 \text{ ampere}$$

then substitute in the power formula:

$$P = I^2 R$$

Circuit 4
Circuit

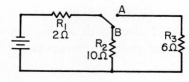

R₁
2Ω

A

B

R₂
10Ω

R₃
6Ω

This is a double series circuit. It differs from Circuit 3 in that *two* resistors will be in series with the battery and switch regardless of the switch position.

86

Problems

1. With the switch in position *B*, which resistors will be in series?
2. With the switch in position *A*, which resistor will have the greatest voltage drop?
3. With the switch in position *A*, which resistors are in parallel?
4. Is it possible to "switch off" this circuit?

Answers

1. With the switch in *B* position, R_1 and R_2 will be in series.
2. With the switch in *A* position, R_3 will have the greater drop.
3. This is a catch question. *No* resistors will be in parallel.
4. No, it is not possible to "switch off" this circuit. One or the other of the two series circuits will always be *"on."* However, the circuit could be modified by installing a *master switch,* as shown in the examples below.

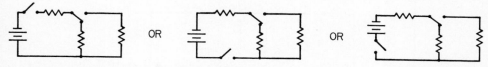

Other combinations are possible, but, a master switch at any of the points (*X*) in the illustration below would work *only* if the main SPDT switch were in position *A*. It would *not* function if the SPDT switch were in position *B*. As a result it would not truly be serving as a master switch.

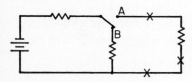

A master switch in any *X* position would *not* function if the single-pole/double-throw switch (SPDT) were in the position shown.

Circuit 5

Circuit

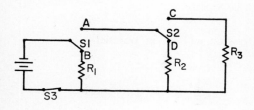

This also is a series circuit, or more correctly, a combination of series circuits. Regardless of the position of either or both switches S_1 or S_2, this circuit could never become a parallel circuit unless modified. Switch S_3 is simply a master switch.

Problems

1. With switch S_1 in position *B*, will R_2 or R_3 experience a voltage drop?
2. With switch S_1 in position *A*, which resistor will have a current flow through it?

3. With switch S_2 in position C, which resistor will experience a voltage drop?
4. With switch S_3 *open*, which resistor will have a voltage drop?

Answers

1. Neither. They will both be in an open circuit.
2. Resistor R_2.
3. R_1 will experience the voltage drop regardless of the position of S_2, since S_2 is an open circuit whenever S_1 is in the position B as shown.
4. This is a catch question. No resistor will have a voltage drop because S_3 is a master switch. Opening it opens *all* circuits regardless of their switch positions.

Circuit 6

Circuit

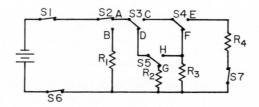

Problems

1. If S_1 is closed, which resistors are in the closed circuit?
2. If S_6 is open, which resistor will be in the closed circuit?
3. If S_2 is in position A, will it matter whether S_7 is open or closed?
4. If S_5 is in position H, and S_4 is in position E, which resistor will be in parallel? Which in series?

Answers

1. R_2 is the only resistor in the closed circuit. It will be in series with the battery, S_1, S_2, S_3, S_6, and S_5.
2. None, since the entire network will be open.
3. No.
4. Resistor R_3 will be in series. No resistor will be in parallel.

Circuit 7

Circuit

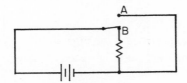

This is a double series circuit, but note a very peculiar characteristic of this particular hookup.

Problems

1. If the switch is in *B* position, how much voltage drop will occur across the resistor?
2. If the switch is in position *A*, what kind of undesirable condition will occur?
3. If the resistor were a light bulb, what would happen if the switch were placed in position *A*, and a jumper wire were placed from point *B* to *A*?
4. What is a "shunt"?

Answers

1. Since there is only *one* resistor the total value of the battery voltage will be dropped across it. If there were *two* resistors of *equal* value, one-half the source voltage would be dropped across one and one-half across the other. If there were two or more resistors of *unequal* value, the amount of voltage dropped across each would depend upon the resistance of each and the current in the circuit.
2. A short circuit would develop because an electrical current will seek the path of least resistance. Since a short circuit represents a nearly zero resistance, the current would flow through it and quickly ruin the battery. Almost none would flow through the resistor even if point *B* had a jumper to point *A* because the electrons would take the path of least resistance — the short circuit!
3. The light bulb would go out. See No. 2 above.
4. A "shunt" is another name for a parallel circuit.

REMEMBER

Current always takes the path of least resistance.

Circuit Problems

■ Problem 1

Which circuit will have the greater total current?

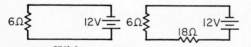

These are series circuits. Any time resistances are added in a *series circuit,* the total resistance becomes *greater*. With a greater total resistance, and voltage remaining the same, amperage must become less.

■ Problem 2

Which circuit will have the greater total current?

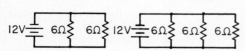

These are parallel circuits. Any time resistances are added to a *parallel circuit,* the total resistance becomes *less*. With a lesser total resistance, and voltage remaining the same, the amperage becomes greater.

■ Problem 3

Look at the following circuit carefully and answer the questions.

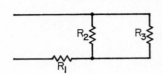

In this series-parallel circuit, _____ and _____ are in parallel. Both of them are in _____ with resistor R_1.

R_2 and R_3 are in parallel. Both of them are in series with R_1.

■ Problem 4

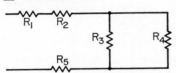

In this series-parallel circuit, R_1 is in _____ with R_2. R_3 and R_4 are in _____ with R_1 and R_2. R_3 is in _____ with all of the other resistors, *except* R_4.

R_1 is in series with R_2. R_3 and R_4 are in series with R_1 and R_2. R_3 is in series with all of the other resistors, except R_4.

Facts About Actual Circuits

Resistors will not always be laid out in neat squares and rectangles. On the contrary! In actual circuits it may be difficult to distinguish a parallel from a series circuit. Correct analysis will come with practice.

Examples

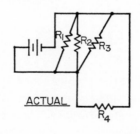

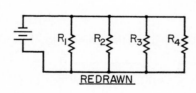

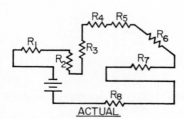

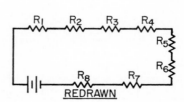

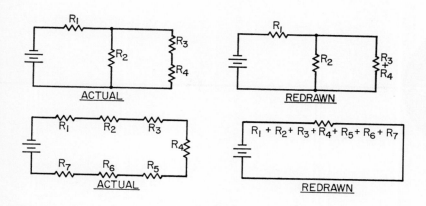

ACTUAL

REDRAWN

ACTUAL

REDRAWN

REVIEW QUESTIONS

1. Will there ever be a voltage drop across a resistor if there is no flow of current through it?

2. If an "open" occurs in any part of a series circuit, what will happen to the flow of current in all other parts of that circuit?

3. If an "open" occurs in any part of a parallel circuit, what will happen to the flow of current in the branch circuits which are not open?

4. How much voltage will be dropped across each resistor in a parallel circuit?

5. If a series circuit has four resistors, all of the same value, and a source voltage of eight volts, how much voltage will be dropped across each resistor?

6. If a series circuit has two resistors, one having five times as much resistance as the other, what will be the ratio of voltage drop across each?

7. If a circuit has a total resistance of 4 ohms, and an amperage of 2 amperes, how much power will be consumed?

8. Draw a series circuit having a battery and two resistors.

9. Draw a parallel circuit having a battery and two resistors.

10. Draw a series-parallel circuit having one resistor in series with two parallel resistors.

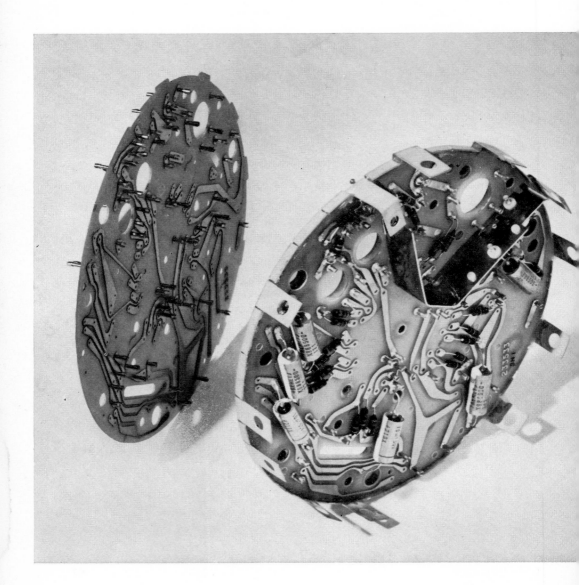

Unit 9

KIRCHHOFF'S LAWS

The importance of understanding circuits cannot be overemphasized. If one desires more than a superficial knowledge of electricity and electronics, he must seek depth in truly understanding circuitry. Thus far you have studied voltage, resistance, and amperage. You know how to calculate resistance — in series, parallel, and series-parallel. You have also had a small amount of practice analyzing different kinds of circuits.

To further provide depth in understanding, two laws will be presented — one law is concerned with current, the other law deals with voltage. They are called *Kirchhoff's Laws* (kerk-hoff).

These laws will assist you in breaking down circuits in such a manner that you can analyze them more easily. You will be better able to determine certain unknown resistances and voltages as well as be able to analyze one or more parts of a total network.

KIRCHHOFF'S FIRST LAW

THE RULE

The current entering a circuit exactly equals the current leaving the circuit.

The current problems you have already dealt with should have proven the above law. Since you were concerned at that time with different applications of the relationship of voltage-resistance-current, you will now take a fresh look at the principles of Kirchhoff's Laws.

Take a look at the following circuits:

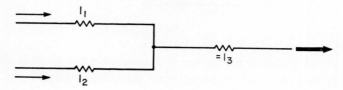

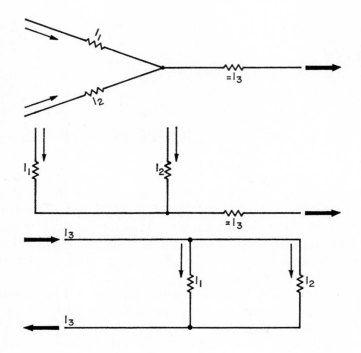

In each case the current entering the circuit is exactly equal to the current leaving the circuit — $I_1 + I_2 = I_3$.

A Closer Look

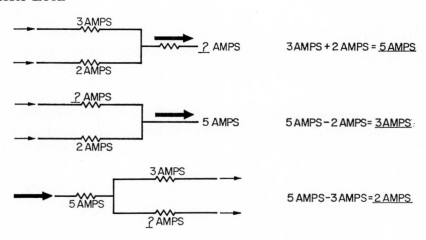

3 AMPS + 2 AMPS = 5 AMPS

5 AMPS − 2 AMPS = 3 AMPS

5 AMPS − 3 AMPS = 2 AMPS

From the above, you can readily see if 2 amperages are given in the problems, one can easily find the third amperage even though it is unknown.

And, how is this accomplished? It is done by applying *Kirchhoff's Law.*

■ A Problem to Solve

Apply Kirchhoff's Law to find the unknowns:

1. What is I_4?
2. What is the current at the junction?

Solving the Problem

A. In the preceding problem you know the total current entering the circuit is 10 amperes. Applying Kirchhoff's Law, you know 10 amperes *must be leaving the circuit.* If $I_3 = 7$ amperes, I_4 must equal the difference between 7 amperes and 10 amperes or an answer of 3 amperes. So: $I_4 = 3$ amperes.

B. Once again applying Kirchhoff's Law you know 10 amperes are entering the circuit. Since the two branches of I_1 and I_2 meet at the junction, the total current, I_t, must also be 10 amperes at the junction.

Another Problem

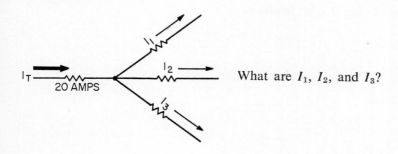

What are I_1, I_2, and I_3?

With the information given it is impossible to determine how much amperage is flowing through any *one* resistor, *but* there is one statement that can be made: *The sum of the currents of* $I_1 + I_2 + I_3$ *must total 20 amperes!*

95

The Law Works for Any Junction

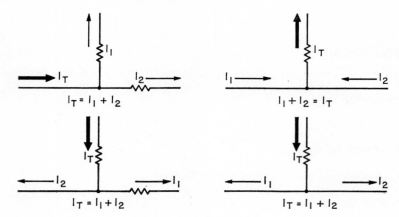

$$I_T = I_1 + I_2$$

$$I_1 + I_2 = I_T$$

$$I_T = I_1 + I_2$$

$$I_T = I_1 + I_2$$

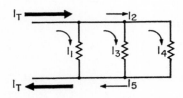

Which statement is false?

A. $I_2 = I_4 + I_3$

B. $I_3 + I_4 = I_5$

C. $I_t = I_4 + I_5 + I_2 + I_3$

Unless you chose *C* as the incorrect answer you have not learned your lesson. *Any* of the following statements would be true, but *C* above is definitely wrong. Can you tell why?

$$I_t = I_1 + I_5$$
$$I_t = I_1 + I_3 + I_4$$
$$I_t = I_1 + I_2$$

Problem Solving Using Light Bulbs

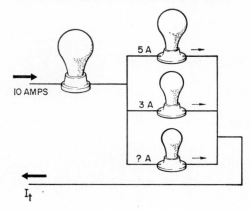

A. What is the total amperage?

B. How many amperes are flowing through the smallest bulb?

A. Casual observation immediately indicates 10 amperes are entering the circuit as well as leaving. This is the total amperage.

B. If there are 10 amperes total, and 8 amperes (5 + 3) are flowing through the top two lamps in the parallel circuit, 2 amperes must be flowing through the smallest lamp (10 − 8).

Problem Solving Using Appliances

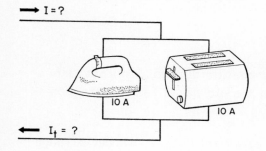

What is the total amperage entering and leaving the circuit?

You can easily determine the total amperage by adding the amperage of the flat iron and the toaster in the parallel circuit.

$$10 \text{ amperes} + 10 \text{ amperes} = 20 \text{ amperes}$$

Problem Solving Using Series Circuits

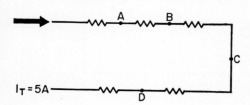

What is the amperage at the following points:

$A = $ _____ amperes
$B = $ _____ amperes
$C = $ _____ amperes
$D = $ _____ amperes

THE RULE

Amperage remains the same throughout a series circuit.

Applying the well known rule that amperage remains the same throughout a series circuit, it must follow that five amperes will be flowing through each and every point. If the total resistance is high, the amperage flow will be low. On the other hand, if the total resistance is low the amperage will be higher for a given voltage. But high or low, it remains the same throughout the entire circuit!

Problem Solving Using Parallel Circuits

Amperage flowing through the indicated points will be as follows:

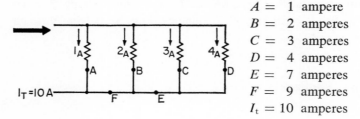

$A =$ 1 ampere
$B =$ 2 amperes
$C =$ 3 amperes
$D =$ 4 amperes
$E =$ 7 amperes
$F =$ 9 amperes
$I_t =$ 10 amperes

THE RULE

Amperage may vary considerably in a parallel circuit, depending upon the individual resistors in each branch circuit.

But: The total amperage entering the circuit will always — without exception — *equal the amperage leaving the circuit.*

How Much Have You learned?

Answer the Questions Concerning the Following Problem

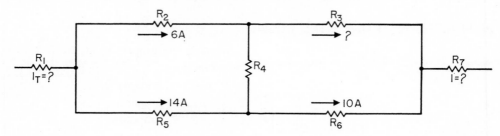

A. What is I_t?
B. How much amperage will flow through R_4?
C. Which direction will amperage flow through R_4?
D. How much amperage will flow through R_3?
E. How much amperage will flow through R_7?
F. Which direction will amperage flow through R_7?

Solutions to the Problems

A. $I_t = 20$ amperes $(R_5 + R_2$ *or* $14 + 6)$.
B. 4 amperes will flow through R_4 $(R_5 - R_6$ *or* $14 - 10)$.
C. The current will flow upward through R_4 ↑.

   Why? If 14 amperes are flowing through R_5 and only 10 amperes through

R_6, there is only one way the current can go — *up!* This is also proven by the fact that R_2 has a lesser amperage than its parallel resistor R_5.

D. 10 amperes will flow through R_3 ($R_2 + R_4$ *or* 6 + 4).

Also, since you know $I_t = 20$, and you also know R_6 is 10 amperes, the amount flowing through R_3 would be $I_t - R_6$ *or* 20 − 10.

E. 20 amperes will flow through R_7, the same as through R_1 which, as you know, is the same as R_t.

F. The current will flow away from the circuit ⟶.

Nodes

The junction of two or more resistors is called a node (noh-d). Electrons flow into and away from a node.

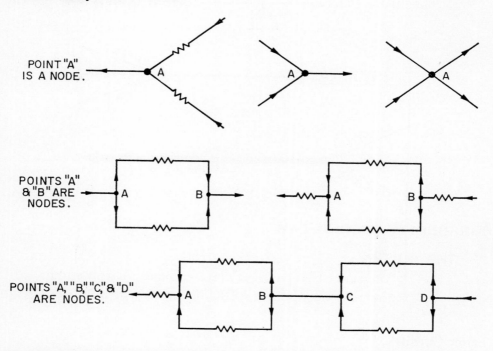

THE RULE

The point at which two or more currents come to-gether and leave is called a NODE.

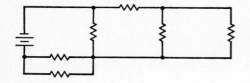

If one were to label all of the nodes in this schematic . . . ,

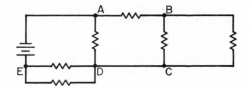

the labeled schematic would look like this:

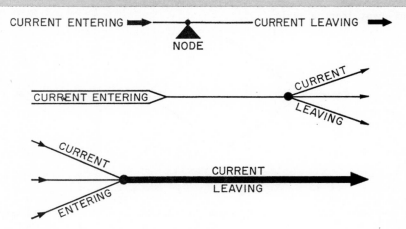

CURRENT ENTERING ➡ — NODE — CURRENT LEAVING ➡

CURRENT ENTERING — CURRENT LEAVING

CURRENT ENTERING — CURRENT LEAVING

KIRCHHOFF'S SECOND LAW

Series Circuits

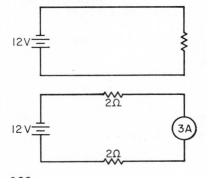

Because there is only *one* resistor in this circuit, the full 12 volts of the source must be dropped across it regardless of its resistance.

Because the two resistors are equal in value, the voltage drop across one will be the same as the drop across the other — 6 volts.

$$E = IR \quad or \quad E = 2 \times 3 = 6 \text{ volts}$$

100

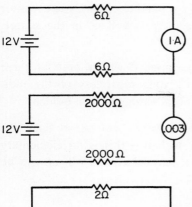

Again the same voltage will be dropped across each resistor because they are of equal value.

$$E = I\,R \quad or \quad E = 1 \times 6 = 6 \text{ volts}$$

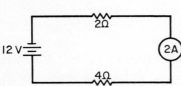

And *again* the same voltage will be dropped across each resistor.

$$E = I\,R \quad or \quad E = .003 \times 2000 = 6 \text{ volts}$$

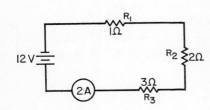

In this circuit 4 volts are dropped across the 2-ohm resistor and 8 volts are dropped across the 4-ohm resistor.

$$E = I\,R \quad or \quad 2 \times 2 = 4$$
$$E = I\,R \quad or \quad 2 \times 4 = 8$$

NOTE: The *sum* of the voltage drops around the circuit equals the applied voltage of the circuit.

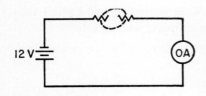

$$I = 2 \text{ amperes} \qquad I = \frac{E}{R_{total}}$$

R_1 drop = 2 volts $\quad(E = I\,R = 2 \times 1)$
R_2 drop = 4 volts $\quad(E = I\,R = 2 \times 2)$
R_3 drop = 6 volts $\quad(E = I\,R = 2 \times 3)$
2 volts + 4 volts + 6 volts = 12 volts

And again Kirchhoff's Second Law is upheld, just as it always will be! The sum of the voltage drops around the circuit equals the voltage applied *across* the circuit.

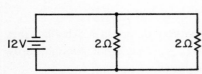

Here, there is no voltage drop across either resistor, and there never will be until the "open" in the circuit is closed.

A voltage drop will *never* occur unless a current is flowing through the circuit.

Parallel Circuits

How much voltage is dropped across each resistor? 6 volts? *No!*

Because the resistors are in *parallel* the *full 12 volts* are dropped across *each resistor.*

Why do not the two voltages add?

The reason is that Kirchhoff's Second Law clearly states the sum of the voltage drops around a circuit equals the voltage applied *across* the circuit.

101

Since a battery is always *across* each resistor in a parallel circuit, each resistor will have the same voltage impressed upon it as there is voltage in the source. Thus:

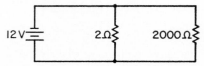

The voltage applied across *both* of these resistors is 12 volts regardless of the individual amperages through each branch.

It is true the resistance of each resistor may vary, and as it does the amperage through each branch resistor will vary with it — this is an elementary application of *Ohm's Law*. But, the voltages in a parallel circuit will *always* be equal to the source voltage.

Series-Parallel Circuits

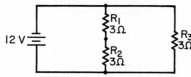

Here is a series-parallel circuit. Resistors R_1 and R_2 are in series, but *both* are in parallel with R_3. *And,* both parallel resistance networks are in parallel with the battery.

The voltage across the branch circuit R_1 and R_2 is 12 volts. Also, the voltage across the branch circuit R_3 is 12 volts. *Each* of these branches is in shunt (parallel) with the other.

But, since R_1 and R_2 are in *series,* there will be an individual voltage drop across *each* of these two resistors. Because both happen to be of equal value, they will drop equal voltages — 6 volts each.

Another Problem

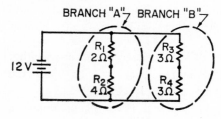

Once again each branch circuit has 12 volts across it.

R_1 and R_2 in branch *A* will have 4 volts and 8 volts dropped respectively.

R_3 and R_4 will *each* have a 6-volt drop.

$$R_1 \text{ drop} = E = I R = 2 \text{ amperes} \times 2 \text{ ohms} = 4 \text{ volts}$$
$$R_2 \text{ drop} = E = I R = 2 \text{ amperes} \times 4 \text{ ohms} = 8 \text{ volts}$$
$$R_3 \text{ and } R_4 \text{ drop} = E = I R = 2 \text{ amperes} \times 6 \text{ ohms} = 12 \text{ volts}$$

RELAYS AND CIRCUITS

Relays are switches. Their mechanical construction determines whether they will be a single-pole/single-throw switch (SPST), a single-pole/double-throw (SPDT), or some other type or combination of types.

Before one can truly understand the operation of a relay, he must understand the principle upon which it works. To accomplish this one must review magnetism.

Magnetism

Just as a + charge will attract a − charge, so will a magnet attract a piece of iron, or the *north pole* of a magnet will attract the *south pole* of another magnet.

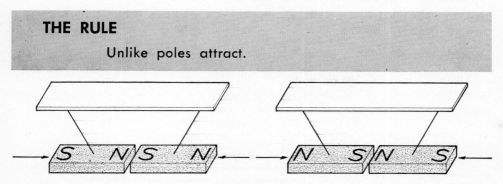

On the other hand, just as a positive charge will repel another positive charge, so will a *south pole* of a magnet repel another *south pole,* and a *north pole* will repel another *north pole.*

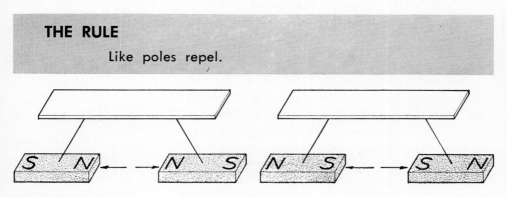

Permanent Magnets

Permanent magnets take many shapes and forms. Some are bar magnets, others horseshoe magnets. Regardless of their shape or size, they work on the same principle: the *magnetic lines of force* which surround the magnet have an attraction or repulsion for other magnets. These magnetic lines of force are sometimes called *lines of flux,* or simply a *magnetic field.*

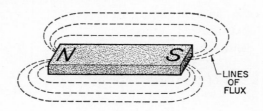

LINES OF FLUX

The closer the magnetic field is to the magnet, the more attraction or repulsion there is — the stronger it is. As the field gets farther from the magnet, the weaker it becomes. It follows, then, the nearer a piece of iron is brought to a magnet, the greater will be the attraction for that magnet. Iron, or any ferrous metal, will always be attracted by a magnet. Relays make use of this very important fact.

Electromagnets

Whenever an electric current travels through a wire, a magnetic field of force surrounds the wire. This field of force is exactly comparable to the magnetic field which surrounds the permanent magnet.

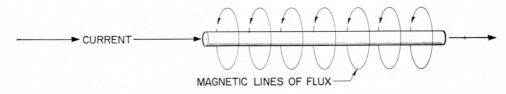

As long as the current is maintained, the magnetic field will remain. When the current stops, the field collapses. The magnetism thus produced is called *electromagnetism*.

If a length of wire is bent to form a loop, the lines of force enter one side of the loop and leave the other side. Adding turns of wire and forming them into a coil increases the total magnetic field of force. The electromagnet becomes stronger.

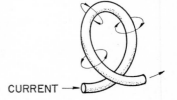

Adding turns of wire and forming them into a coil increases the total magnetic lines of force.

Iron has less opposition (reluctance) to the lines of force than does air. Adding an iron core to the coil concentrates the magnetic lines of force and makes the electromagnet even stronger. The flux density has then been increased.

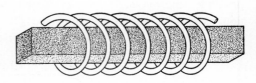

The symbol for a coil of wire with an air core is:

The symbol for a coil having an iron core is: 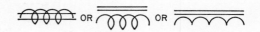 OR OR

A coil of wire having an electric current passing through it is called an electromagnet.

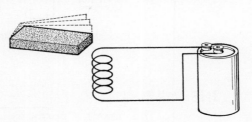

When current flows through an electromagnet, the magnetic lines of force will attract iron.

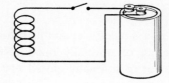

When no current flows no magnetic field is present. There is no attraction.

An electromagnet can be constructed to form an electrically-operated switch.

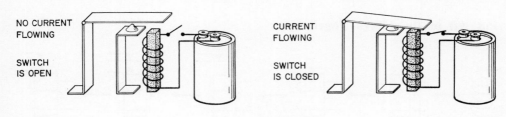

NO CURRENT
FLOWING

SWITCH
IS OPEN

CURRENT
FLOWING

SWITCH
IS CLOSED

Using symbols:

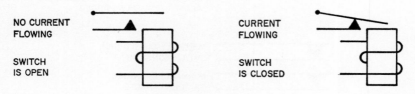

NO CURRENT
FLOWING

SWITCH
IS OPEN

CURRENT
FLOWING

SWITCH
IS CLOSED

All relays do not have single-pole/single-throw switch contacts. There are many combinations. Shown here is a single-pole/double-throw switch.

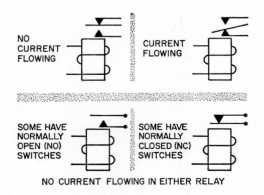

SOME HAVE NORMALLY OPEN (NO) SWITCHES | SOME HAVE NORMALLY CLOSED (NC) SWITCHES

NO CURRENT FLOWING IN EITHER RELAY

THE RULE

The terms "normally open" (NO) and "normally closed" (NC) are always so indicated with NO current flowing.

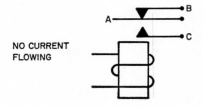

NO CURRENT FLOWING

This is a single-pole/double-throw switch. It has one set of normally open (NO) contacts and one set of normally closed (NC) contacts. The arm is *A*, the NC is *B*, and the NO is *C*.

Put All of the Pieces Together

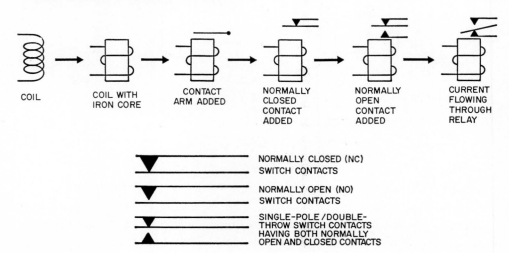

COIL | COIL WITH IRON CORE | CONTACT ARM ADDED | NORMALLY CLOSED CONTACT ADDED | NORMALLY OPEN CONTACT ADDED | CURRENT FLOWING THROUGH RELAY

NORMALLY CLOSED (NC) SWITCH CONTACTS

NORMALLY OPEN (NO) SWITCH CONTACTS

SINGLE-POLE/DOUBLE-THROW SWITCH CONTACTS HAVING BOTH NORMALLY OPEN AND CLOSED CONTACTS

Circuits Using Relays

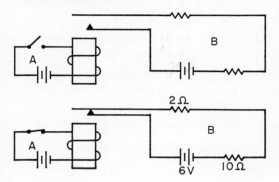

No current flowing in circuit *A*. With no current flowing, the electro-magnet is not energized and the NO switch remains open. With the NO contacts open, no current flows in *B*.

With the switch in circuit *A* closed, the relay is energized. The NO switch contacts close and ½ ampere flows in circuit *B*.

With switch *A* closed circuit *B* is closed and circuit *C* open, 4 amperes flow in *B*.

When switch opens, circuit *B* opens and circuit *C* closes. No amperage flows in *B*, but 2 amperes flow in *C*.

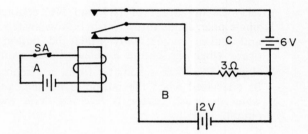

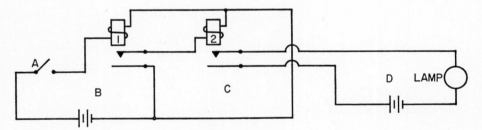

When One Relay Controls Another

When switch *A* is manually closed relay *1* is energized closing contacts *B*. This energizes relay *2* which closes contacts *C*. With switch *C* closed, circuit *D* is energized and the lamp lights.

REVIEW QUESTIONS

1. State Kirchhoff's First Law in your own words.

2. State Kirchhoff's Second Law in your own words.

3. If 5 amperes enter a circuit, how many amperes must be leaving the circuit?

4. If 3 amperes are entering wire *A* and 4 amperes entering wire *B,* how many amperes must be flowing away from wire *C* which is connected to *A* and *B*?

5. A complement of 5 resistors in series has the following voltage drops: 5 volts, 10 volts, 15 volts, 25 volts, 50 volts. What is the voltage applied across the circuit?

6. A complement of 3 resistors in parallel have the following voltage drops: 6 volts, 6 volts, 6 volts. What is the voltage applied across the circuit?

7. A friend tells you he has designed a parallel circuit having two resistors having the following voltage drops: 6 volts, and 12 volts. What will you tell your friend?

8. Draw the schematic diagram for a relay with NO contact points.

9. Draw the schematic diagram for a relay with NC contact points.

10. You are given the following components:
   1 battery
   1 relay having a set of NO and NC contact points
   1 single-pole/single-throw push button switch. The switch is normally open and makes contact *only* while the button is depressed. It immediately opens when the button is released (the same as a doorbell button).

   Problem: Draw, in schematic form, a circuit which will cause the relay to be energized when the button is pushed, *and* which will *remain energized* when the push button is *released*. You will then have a "lock-in" relay circuit.

Unit 10

WORKING WITH VERY LARGE AND VERY SMALL NUMBERS

In electronics it is not uncommon to work with an amperage as small as $\frac{1}{1000}$, or a resistor having a value of 1,000,000 ohms. Writing numbers such as $\frac{1}{1,000,000}$ (.000001) or 1,000,000 is unhandy and many times confusing.

You have already been introduced to the powers of numbers. This method of dealing with very large and very small numbers will now be expanded, and will serve as the foundation upon which you will build a new electronics vocabulary.

It is interesting. It is important. And it is fun!

Multiples of 10

The figure "1" can take on many different values depending upon the position of the decimal point. Study the following examples carefully. Think about them. Learn the significance of each, and use them as tools which will work for you whether you are studying electronics, astrophysics, or farming.

$$\begin{aligned}
1. &\text{ is the same as } 1 \times 1 \\
10. &\text{ is the same as } 1 \times 10 \\
100. &\text{ is the same as } 1 \times 10 \times 10 \\
1,000. &\text{ is the same as } 1 \times 10 \times 10 \times 10 \\
10,000. &\text{ is the same as } 1 \times 10 \times 10 \times 10 \times 10
\end{aligned}$$

Now, then, if you learned your previous lessons well, you know it is not necessary to add all of the zeros behind the "1" in order to indicate values greater than "1." You can use powers of 10 instead. Thus:

$$1 = 10^0$$
$$10 = 10^1 \text{ (or } 1 \times 10^1)$$
$$100 = 10^2 \text{ (or } 1 \times 10^2)$$
$$1000 = 10^3 \text{ (or } 1 \times 10^3)$$
$$10000 = 10^4 \text{ (or } 1 \times 10^4)$$

In order to determine the power number, one has only to ask, "How many times must 10 be multiplied times itself in order to equal the given number?" Thus:

$$10 \times 10 = 100 \quad \text{or } 10^2$$
$$10 \times 10 \times 10 = 1000 \text{ or } 10^3$$
and so on.

An even easier method is to simply count the number of zeros following the first digit. That number will represent the power number. Thus:

$$1000 = 10^3$$
$$100000 = 10^5$$

(In reality you are counting the number of times the decimal point has been moved to the right of the first digit.)

Numbers Other Than Multiples of 10

Numbers other than multiples of 10 may also be written with power numbers. Thus:

150	becomes	1.5×10^2
1500	becomes	1.5×10^3
15,000,000	becomes	1.5×10^7
15,000,000,000,000,000	becomes	1.5×10^{16}

or:

550	becomes	5.5×10^2
5500	becomes	5.5×10^3
550,000	becomes	5.5×10^5
55,000,000,000,000,000	becomes	5.5×10^{16}

Moving Decimal Places

Moving the decimal point to the *right* makes the number *larger*.

1.00000000

In the above number it does not matter how many zeros are added after the decimal point. The value is just "1," unless the decimal point is moved or unless a value digit is added.

But . . . 1.00000.000

Moving the decimal point 5 places to the right changes the number to 100,000. or 10^5 or 1×10^5.

Moving the decimal point to the *left* in a number makes it *smaller*.

$$1. = 1$$
$$.1 = \tfrac{1}{10} \quad or \quad 1 \div 10$$
$$.01 = \tfrac{1}{100} \quad or \quad 1 \div 100$$
$$.001 = \tfrac{1}{1000} \quad or \quad 1 \div 1000$$

These smaller-than-1 numbers can also be written in powers of 1. Thus:

$$.1 = 1 \times 10^{-1}$$
$$.01 = 1 \times 10^{-2}$$
$$.001 = 1 \times 10^{-3}$$
$$.0001 = 1 \times 10^{-4}$$
$$.00001 = 1 \times 10^{-5}$$

NOTE: The number of places the decimal point is moved from 1.0 are counted and determine the negative power number.

Moving the decimal point from 1.0 may be *either* to the right or the left. It may also be moved to the right or left of any other number or numbers and its power of 10 noted. Thus:

$$1.5 = 1.5 \times 10^0$$
$$.15 = 1.5 \times 10^{-1}$$
$$.015 = 1.5 \times 10^{-2}$$
$$.0015 = 1.5 \times 10^{-3}$$

or

$$.0655 = 6.55 \times 10^{-2}$$
$$.00655 = 6.55 \times 10^{-3}$$
$$.0000000655 = 6.55 \times 10^{-8}$$

or

$$.655 = 6.55 \times 10^{-1}$$
$$.000655 = 6.55 \times 10^{-4}$$
$$.00000000655 = 6.55 \times 10^{-9}$$

try some more:

$$45.678 = 4.5678 \times 10^1$$
$$255,000,000 = 2.55 \times 10^8$$
$$56,000,000 = 5.6 \times 10^7$$

Once again, it is really the decimal point which is being moved and which is being counted each time it is moved!

$$.000006 = 6 \times 10^{-6}$$
$$.00561234 = 5.61234 \times 10^{-3}$$
$$.0714321 = 7.14321 \times 10^{-2}$$

1 coulomb = 6,280,000,000,000,000,000 electrons, *or* 6.28×10^{18}

Try a Few More

$$1.5 \times 10^2 = 150$$
$$1.5 \times 10^{-2} = .015$$
$$1.5 \times 10^1 = 15$$
$$1.5 \times 10^3 = 1500$$
$$1.5 \times 10^7 = 15,000,000$$
$$1 \times 10^{-2} = .01$$
$$1.5 \times 10^{-2} = .015$$
$$1.5 \times 10^{-3} = .0015$$
$$1 \times 10^6 = 1,000,000$$

113

Exponents

The small number above and to the right of the 10 (below) is called the *exponent* (eks-*poe*-nent).

$$2 \text{ is the exponent in } 10^2$$
$$3 \text{ is the exponent in } 10^3$$
$$4 \text{ is the exponent in } 10^4$$
$$5 \text{ is the exponent in } 10^5$$

THE RULE
Multiplying powers of 10 is the same as ADDING their exponents.

Thus:

$$10^1 \times 10^2 = 10^3 \quad (1 + 2 = 3)$$
$$10^2 \times 10^3 = 10^5$$
$$10^5 \times 10^5 = 10^{10}$$
$$10^9 \times 10^9 = 10^{18}$$

Try Some Conversions

$$1000 \times 10,000 = 10^3 \times 10^4 \quad or \quad 10^7 \quad or \quad 10,000,000$$
$$10 \times 100 = 10^1 \times 10^2 \quad or \quad 10^3 \quad or \quad 1000$$

THE RULE
If the exponents involve both positive and negative numbers, subtract the smaller from the larger, and use the sign of the larger in the answer.

$$10^5 \times 10^{-2} = 10^3 \quad (5 - 2 = 3)$$
$$10^{-2} \times 10^6 = 10^4$$
$$10^6 \times 10^{-8} = 10^{-2}$$

THE RULE
When multiplying more than 1 number, add all exponents and multiply the remaining numbers.

$$(2 \times 10^2) \times (2 \times 10^2) = 4 \times 10^4 \quad or \quad 40,000$$
$$(2 \times 10^2) \times (2 \times 10^4) = 4 \times 10^6 \quad or \quad 4,000,000$$
$$(4 \times 10^5) \times (2 \times 10^{-2}) = 8 \times 10^3 \quad or \quad 8000$$
$$(4 \times 10^5) \times (2 \times 10^{-8}) = 8 \times 10^{-3} \quad or \quad .008$$

$$(2 \times 10^2) \times (2 \times 10^4) \times (7 \times 10^{12}) = 2.8 \times 10^{19}$$

$$(4 \times 10^4) \times (1.57 \times 10^{19}) \times (1 \times 10^{-5}) = 6.28 \times 10^{18}$$

A New Vocabulary

Electricity and electronics have many new and interesting words. Some of these words represent the powers of ten you have been studying. Examine the following terms carefully:

$$\text{Kilo} = 1000 \quad or \quad 10^3$$
$$\text{Mega} = 1,000,000 \quad or \quad 10^6$$
$$\text{Milli} = \tfrac{1}{1000} \quad or \quad 10^{-3}$$
$$\text{Micro} = \tfrac{1}{1,000,000} \quad or \quad 10^{-6}$$

Actually the above are not words but *prefixes* which are added to *other words,* such as:

Kilo $\longrightarrow$ 1 *kilo*watt = 1000 watts
or, 1 kilowatt = 10^3 watts $\longleftarrow$ 1×10^3 watt

Mega $\longrightarrow$ 1 *meg*ohm = 1,000,000 ohms
or, 1 megohm = 10^6 ohms $\longleftarrow$ 1×10^6 ohms

Milli $\longrightarrow$ 1 *milli*ampere = .001 ampere
or, 1 milliampere = 10^{-3} ampere $\longleftarrow$ 1×10^{-3} ampere

Micro $\longrightarrow$ 1 *micro*ampere = .000001 ampere
or, 1 microampere = 10^{-6} ampere $\longleftarrow$ 1×10^{-6} ampere

Million = mega $\rightarrow$ (example: megacycle)
Thousand = kilo $\rightarrow$ (example: kilocycle)
Thousandth = milli $\rightarrow$ (example: millivolt)
Millionth = micro $\rightarrow$ (example: microvolt)

In all of the preceding applications the new terms served as prefixes to words you already know. In only one case was the prefix changed:

instead of saying meg*a*ohm, the "a" was dropped and it became megohm.

It is very common to find electrical units measured in "milli's," "micro's," "kilo's," and "mega's." The electrical power used in your home is measured in kilowatts. All radio and television circuits have amperages in milliamperes, and they have resistors having values expressed in megohms. Radio and television stations transmit on certain frequencies measured in kilocycles and megacycles.

Just as other electrical terms have symbols and abbreviations, so have the new prefixes you have just learned.

115

$$kilo = K$$
$$mega = M$$
$$milli = m$$
$$micro = \mu \text{ or } mu$$

or

1 K = 1,000	1 K = 1×10^3
2 M = 2,000,000	2 M = 2×10^6
6 m = .006	6 m = 6×10^{-3}
6 μ = .000006	6 μ = 6×10^{-6}

Following are problems using these very large and very small numbers. You will also find use for the new vocabulary.

Problem

A radio circuit having a current of 3 ma (3 milliamperes) flowing through a 2 Ω (2 ohms) resistance must have how many volts of pressure pushing the electrons through the circuit?

Given: I = 3 ma.   (3×10^{-3})
       R = 2 Ω
       E = ?

Formula: E = I R

Substitute and solve: E = (3×10^{-3}) × 2
               = 6×10^{-3}
               = 6 mv.   *or*   6 millivolts

A Danger Involved

There is a danger involved in using the new *vocabulary*. Take an example involving this aspect:

10 kilohms × 20 kiloamperes does *not* equal 200 kilovolts (E = I R).
On the contrary! It equals 200 *mega*volts, *not* 200 *kilo*volts.
Work it out the "long way" and see for yourself:

    E = I R
    10,000 ohms × 20,000 amperes = 200,000,000 megavolts

Could the problem have been worked using powers of 10? Absolutely! In fact, this is one of the many advantages of using powers of 10. In solving problems using the new prefix vocabulary, *always* change the values to powers of 10 and solve the problem. See the next page.

Again investigate the problem when it is stated in narrative form:

Problem

Given: I = 20 kiloamperes

R = 10 kilohms

E = ?

Formula: E = I R

Change to powers of 10:   20 kiloamperes = (2.0×10^4)

10 kilohms = (1.0×10^4)

Substitute and solve: E = I R

$= (2.0 \times 10^4) \times (1.0 \times 10^4)$

$= 2.0 \times 10^8$

$= 200{,}000{,}000$ volts   *or*   200 megavolts

Another Problem

How much wattage is consumed by a circuit having 2 kilovolts pushing three kiloamperes through an electric heater?

Given: E = 2 kilovolts

I = 3 kiloamperes

W = ?

Formula: W = E I

Change values to powers of 10:   2 kilovolts $= (2 \times 10^3)$

3 kiloamperes $= (3 \times 10^3)$

Substitute and solve: W = E I

$= (2 \times 10^3) \times (3 \times 10^3)$

$= 6 \times 10^6$

$= 6{,}000{,}000$ watts   *or*   6 megawatts

Dividing Powers of 10

When dividing one power of 10 by another power of 10, *change the sign of the denominator* and add exponents.

Sign changed to negative

Thus: $\dfrac{10^6}{10^2} = 10^6 \times 10^{-2} = 10^4$

Another Example

$$\frac{10^8}{10^4} = 10^8 \times 10^{-4} = 10^4$$

Working With Positive and Negative Signs

■ Problem 1

changed

$$\frac{10^8}{10^{-4}} = 10^8 \times 10^4 = 10^{12}$$

■ Problem 2

$$\frac{10^{-8}}{10^4} = 10^{-8} \times 10^{-4} = 10^{-12}$$

■ Problem 3

$$\frac{6 \times 10^3}{2 \times 10^5} = \frac{6}{2} \times 10^3 \times 10^{-5} = 3 \times 10^{-2}$$

■ Problem 4

$$\frac{6 \times 10^{-3}}{2 \times 10^5} = \frac{6}{2} \times 10^{-3} \times 10^{-5} = 3 \times 10^{-8}$$

■ Problem 5

$$\frac{6 \times 10^3}{2 \times 10^{-5}} = \frac{6}{2} \times 10^3 \times 10^5 = 3 \times 10^8$$

■ Problem 6

$$\frac{6 \times 10^{-3}}{2 \times 10^{-5}} = \frac{6}{2} \times 10^{-3} \times 10^5 = 3 \times 10^2$$

Here are some problems with their answers. Can you determine how the answers were secured?

Given: 50 kilowatts; 25 amps
What is the voltage?
Answer: 2 kilovolts   *or* 2×10^3

Given: 12 megavolts; 2 megohms
What is the amperage?
Answer: 6 amperes

Given: A series circuit having one 3-megohm resistor, one 2-kilohm resistor, and one 100-ohm resistor.
What is the total resistance?
Answer: 3,002,100 ohms

NOTE: The above problem incorporates *addition,* but one cannot simply *add* exponents. (Remember, in working with powers of 10, *addition* is used in *multiplication* or *division, not* in addition. This may seem like double talk until you stop to think about it.

If you were to add exponents in the above problem you would secure an answer of 6×10^{11} or 600,000,000,000 ohms — a ridiculous answer.

Working the problem the "long way" proves 6×10^{11} is wrong:

$$
\begin{aligned}
3 \text{ megohms} &= 3,000,000 \text{ ohms} \\
2 \text{ kilohms} &= 2,000 \text{ ohms} \\
100 \text{ ohms} &= \underline{100 \text{ ohms}} \\
& 3,002,100 \text{ ohms total}
\end{aligned}
$$

One More Problem

Given: A series circuit having one 5-megohm resistor, one 200-kilohm resistor. What is the total resistance?

Answer: 5,200,000 ohms (*or* 5.2 megohms *or* 5.2×10^6 ohms)

REVIEW QUESTIONS

1. Write the power of 10 for 100.

2. Write the power of 10 for 10,000.

3. Write the power of 10 for 1,000,000.

4. Write the power of 10 for .01.

5. Write the power of 10 for .001.

6. Write the power of 10 for .000001.

7. Write the power of 10 for .000000000001.

8. Write the power of 10 for 1500.

9. Write the power of 10 for 150.

10. Write the power of 10 for 15,000.

11. Write the power of 10 for .015.

12. What is the exponent of 10^3?

13. What is the exponent of 10^6?

14. What is the exponent of 10^{-3}?

15. Write the power of 10 for "kilo."

16. Write the power of 10 for "mega."

17. Write the power of 10 for "milli."

18. Write the power of 10 for "micro."

19. Write the power of 10 for "K."

20. Write the power of 10 for "M."

21. Write the power of 10 for "m."

22. Write the power of 10 for "μ."

23. Convert 2 amperes to milliamperes.

24. Convert 2 amperes to microamperes.

25. Convert 10 milliamperes to amperes.

26. Convert 10 milliamperes to microamperes.

27. Convert 1 megacycle to kilocycles.

28. Convert 1.2 megacycles to cycles.

29. Convert 5.6 kilocycles to cycles.

30. Convert 7600 cycles to kilocycles.

31. Convert 6,600,000 cycles to megacycles.

32. Convert 1.3 microamperes to amperes.

33. Convert 125 milliamperes to amperes.

34. Convert .25 ampere to milliamperes.

35. Convert .1 ampere to milliamperes.

Unit 11

CAPACITANCE

Capacitors

A component often found in electrical circuits is the capacitor (kah-*pass*-i-tor). The capacitor is sometimes known as a condenser. The symbol for a capacitor is

OR

The curved line of the first symbol indicates that side of the capacitor which should be connected to ground if a ground connection is needed.

—GROUND THIS SIDE   LIKE THIS—

The positive and negative terminals of a capacitor (condenser) are sometimes labeled.

A capacitor will store an electrical charge. You will remember that an object becomes electrically charged when it contains an excess of either positive or negative charges. Protons are positively charged. Electrons are negatively charged. One coulomb is equivalent to an electrical charge having 6.28×10^{18} negatively charged electrons.

The Unit of Capacitance

A capacitor which can store 1 coulomb of negatively charged electrons when a pressure of one volt is applied is said to have a capacitance of one *farad* (*fair*-add).

123

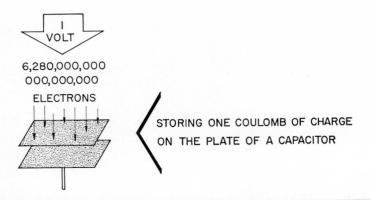

1 VOLT

6,280,000,000
000,000,000
ELECTRONS

STORING ONE COULOMB OF CHARGE
ON THE PLATE OF A CAPACITOR

REMEMBER

The farad is a unit of capacitance. The symbol for capacitance is "C."

The farad rating of a capacitor is a measure of its ability to store an electrical charge.

Because the farad is an unusually *large* value, the rating of capacitors is usually in microfarads (millionths of a farad or 10^{-6}) or in micromicrofarads (millionth millionth or 10^{-12}).

The abbreviation for capacitance is C. The abbreviation for farad is f. A microfarad is abbreviated to mf *or* μf. *A micromicrofarad is abbreviated to* mmf *or* μμf.

■ **Review of Capacitance Symbols**

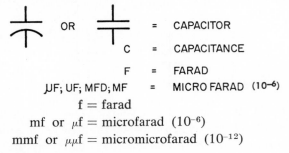

OR	=	CAPACITOR
C	=	CAPACITANCE
F	=	FARAD
μF; UF; MFD; MF	=	MICRO FARAD (10⁻⁶)

f = farad

mf or μf = microfarad (10^{-6})

mmf or μμf = micromicrofarad (10^{-12})

How Capacitors Are Made

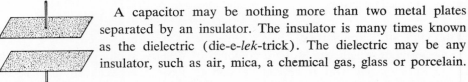

A capacitor may be nothing more than two metal plates separated by an insulator. The insulator is many times known as the dielectric (die-e-*lek*-trick). The dielectric may be any insulator, such as air, mica, a chemical gas, glass or porcelain.

Capacitors are sometimes made using aluminum foil with waxed paper as the insulating dielectric. To conserve space the layers of foil and waxed paper are rolled into tight cylinders with a lead attached to each aluminum strip and projected from either end of the cylinder.

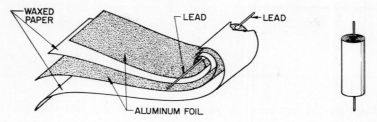

Charging a Capacitor

A capacitor may be charged by connecting it to a battery.

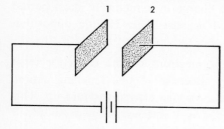

Can you guess what will happen here? Is the circuit complete?

When the battery is first connected electrons flow onto one plate from a pole of the battery. It is impossible for the current to continue on to the remaining pole because of the insulator between the two plates of the capacitor. Thus, a capacitor effectively *blocks the flow of a direct current.*

Something else also happens.

As the electrons pile up on one plate, they repel electrons away from plate 2. At the same time — because opposite charges attract — the negatively charged plate 1 attracts positive charges to plate 2. Therefore, a flow of current *will continue* until the charge on the capacitor equals, or nearly equals, the charge of the battery. The two plates of the capacitor are thus oppositely charged and will remain charged until the battery is disconnected and the charges are somehow permitted to neutralize one another. The latter could be accomplished by shorting the two plates together with a piece of wire.

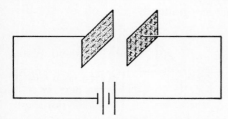

Negative charges pile up on one plate and positive charges on the other, but current cannot continue to flow because of the dielectric.

It takes a definite period of time for the plates of a capacitor to accept a charge equal to the source voltage.

125

The charge in volts and the time it takes a capacitor to become charged can be plotted on a graph.

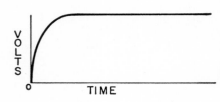

It should be noted the curve rises sharply from the zero point, then rises less sharply, and finally levels out to a straight line horizontally.

There are very important reasons for the shape of the curve. Study the causes listed below.

1. The sharp rise in the curve is made possible by the fact that the capacitor is neutral as the battery is first connected. Because it is neutral there is little opposition to the flow of charge (electrons), and a relatively *large* amount of current will flow in a short period of time. Stating this another way, one might say the capacitor takes on a voltage charge in a relatively short period of time when the battery is *first* connected because there is little opposition to the electron flow.

2. As the capacitor plates become charged the electrons on the capacitor repel more oncoming electrons from the battery. Because of this repelling action, it takes a longer period of time for a greater voltage charge to build up. This is indicated by the curve rising less sharply as it extends away from the *0* point on the graph.

   As the charge on the capacitor becomes more nearly the same as the battery voltage a longer and longer period of time is spent building the charge to its maximum.

3. As the charge on the capacitor reaches the same potential as the battery the curve becomes a horizontal line.

REMEMBER

Thus, it can be stated that capacitance opposes a change in voltage.

A Capacitor Holds Its Charge

If the battery is completely removed from the circuit, the capacitor will continue to hold its charge until the excess charges gradually leak off or are discharged through another circuit.

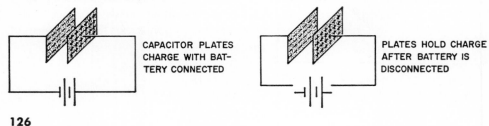

CAPACITOR PLATES CHARGE WITH BATTERY CONNECTED

PLATES HOLD CHARGE AFTER BATTERY IS DISCONNECTED

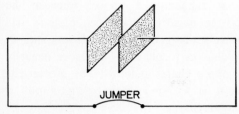

JUMPER

If a jumper wire is connected the positive and negative charges attract one another and the plates once again become neutral.

The above procedure can be illustrated with the use of schematic diagrams:

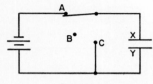

With the switch in position *A*, plates *X* and *Y* of the capacitor become charged.

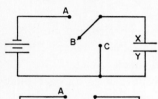

With the switch in position *B*, neither the battery nor the shorting wire is in the circuit. The capacitor holds its charge.

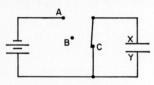

With the switch in position *C*, the shorting wire permits the charge to neutralize.

Factors Affecting Capacitance

There are many factors which affect the amount of charge a capacitor will hold. The larger the capacitor, the closer the plates, and the better the dielectric, the greater the charge a capacitor can hold.

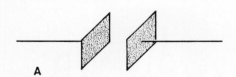

Capacitor *A* holds less charge than capacitor *B*. One can easily understand *the larger* the plates of a capacitor, the more electrons and protons they are able to hold, and *the more capacitance they have.*

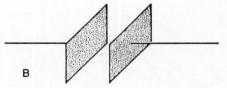

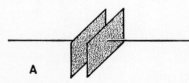

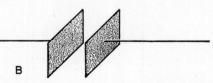

Capacitor *A* holds more charge than *B*. Although this is more difficult to understand it is nonetheless true. As the plates come closer together, each plate

127

has more effect upon the other. Look at capacitor *A* above. Because the plates of this capacitor are close together the negative charge on plate 1 will have more opportunity to repel the negatively charged electrons from plate 2, and at the same time attract more positive charges to plate 2. The more negative plate 1 becomes in relation to plate 2, the more charge it holds. The greater the charge each plate has the more difficult it is to force more charge upon it because it will more strongly repel any similar charge.

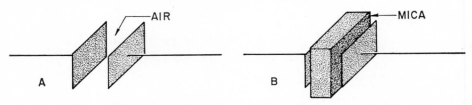

Although the plates of capacitors *A* and *B* are the same size and are separated by the same distance, capacitor *B* will have more capacitance. This is true because *A* has air as its dielectric, while *B* has mica. Since *B* has the better dielectric, it will be able to accept a higher opposite charge on each plate without having that charge leak across from one to the other.

Capacitance and Voltage

THE RULE

capacitance represents **opposition** to a voltage change.

Capacitance resists or opposes changes in voltage.

As voltage attempts to rise (increase), capacitance tends to hold it down.

As voltage attempts to decrease, capacitance tends to hold it up.

The amount of charge a capacitor is able to store is dependent upon the voltage applied and the capacitance of the capacitor.

THE FORMULA

$$Q = V \times C$$

CHARGE $=$ VOLTAGE $\times$ CAPACITANCE
(coulombs) $=$ (volts) $\times$ (farads)

A capacitor having a rating of 30 mfd with 200 volts impressed upon it will have _____?_____ coulombs of charge stored?

Formula:

$Q = V\,C$

Substitute and Solve:

$200 \times (30 \times 10^{-6}) = 6$ millicoulomb (.006 coulomb or 6×10^{-3})

In the preceding problem it must be noted the *formula* states capacitance in *farads,* not in microfarads. Because the problem gave the capacitance in *micro*farads, it had to be converted to *farads* before the problem could be solved. Thus:

30 mfd $= .000030$ farads *or* 30×10^{-6}

Try One More Problem

A capacitor is rated at 20 mfds and 150 volts. If it is functioning at its rated capacity, what is the charge upon its plates?

$Q = V\,C$

$\quad = 150 \times (20 \times 10^{-6})$

$\quad = .003$ coulolmb (or 3 millicoulombs, or 3×10^{-3} coulomb)

One More

A *small* mica capacitor has a capacitance of 250 *mmfd*. If 100 volts are applied, what will be its charge? (*Careful!* The capacitance is stated in *micro*microfarads (10^{-12}).

$Q = V\,C$

$\quad = (1 \times 10^{2}) \times (250 \times 10^{-12})$

$\quad = .000000025000$ coulomb, or 2.5×10^{-8} coulomb

Summarizing

A capacitor is an electrical component used to store an electrical charge. Capacitance is the ratio of the charge stored to the voltage producing the charge. The unit of capacitance is the farad. It is said that one farad exists when a charge of one coulomb of electrons can be stored on the plate of a capacitor as one volt is applied. The factors affecting capacitance are (1) plate size; (2) spacing of the plates; (3) type of dielectric used. The amount of charge a capacitor can hold is dependent upon its capacitance and the applied voltage.

$$\mathbf{Q} = \mathbf{V} \times \mathbf{C} \quad \text{or COULOMBS} = \text{VOLTS} \times \text{FARADS}$$

Connecting Capacitors in Parallel

Capacitance may be increased by the manner in which two or more capacitors are connected together. You already know capacitance may be increased by increasing plate size. This same idea may be used when connecting two or more capacitors in parallel. In effect one is increasing plate size when connecting capacitors in parallel.

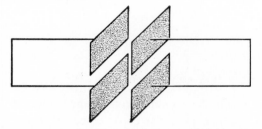

Connecting capacitors in parallel effectively increases plate size.

THE RULE

When capacitors are connected in parallel, capacitance ADDS.

You will note this is exactly *opposite* a resistor. In connecting resistors, a parallel connection causes the resistance to become less. There need be no confusion, however, if one reasons out the difference: resistors in parallel provide more paths over which electrons travel, thus total resistance is less. *But,* capacitors in parallel effectively *add* total plate area, thus making it possible to store more electrons and thereby creating a higher capacitance.

Capacitors in parallel add capacitance.

■ Some Problems

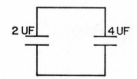

Total capacitance = 2 mfd + 4 mfd = 6 mfd
or .000006 farad
or 6×10^{-6} f

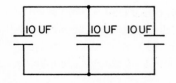

Total capacitance = 10 mfd + 10 mfd + 10 mfd
= 30 mfd
or .000030 f
or 3×10^{-5} farad

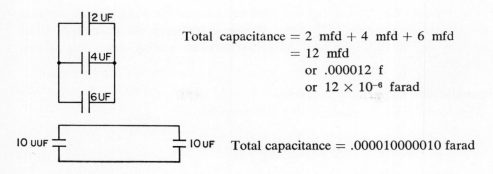

Total capacitance = 2 mfd + 4 mfd + 6 mfd
= 12 mfd
or .000012 f
or 12×10^{-6} farad

Total capacitance = .000010000010 farad

Remember: Microfarads and micromicrofarads are *not* the same thing! It also should be pointed out that this combination would almost *never* be seen in actual circuitry. It is given here only as a matter of illustration.

REMEMBER

Capacitors in PARALLEL add.

Connecting Capacitors in Series

You already know it is possible to *decrease* the capacitance of a capacitor by placing the two plates farther apart. This same idea can be used in connecting capacitors. If two or more capacitors are connected in series the thickness of the dielectric is effectively increased, thus spacing the plates farther apart. This results in a *decrease* in total capacitance.

A ⊣⊢ CAPACITOR 'A' HAS MORE CAPACITANCE THAN 'B' ⊣⊢ B ⊣⊢ The two capacitors connected in series have effectively increased the thickness of the dielectric. Result is the same as in capacitor *B*.

THE RULE

When capacitors are connected in series, the total capacitance becomes less — less than the capacitance of the smallest capacitor in the circuit.

Again you will note this is the opposite of resistors. And again there need be no confusion if the problem is reasoned out. Resistors in series add because the longer a current is forced to flow through a resistance the fewer electrons will flow. *But,* capacitors in series provide a lesser capacitance because the dielectric thickness and spacing between the plates are effectively increased.

The formula for determining the total capacitance for capacitors in series is very similar to resistors in parallel. If you experienced no difficulty figuring resistance in parallel, you will have no difficulty solving series capacitance problems.

Formulas for Capacitors in Series

The formula for a circuit having two capacitors is:

$$C_t = \frac{C_1 \times C_2}{C_1 + C_2}$$

The reciprocal formula for a circuit having more than two capacitors in series is:

$$C_t = \frac{1}{\dfrac{1}{C_1} + \dfrac{1}{C_2} + \dfrac{1}{C_3} + \text{etc.}}$$

■ Some Problems

1. What is the total capacitance?

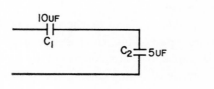

$$C_t = \frac{C_1 \times C_2}{C_1 + C_2}$$

$$= \frac{10 \times 5}{10 + 5}$$

$$= \frac{50}{15} = 3.333 \text{ mfd}$$

2. What is the total capacitance?

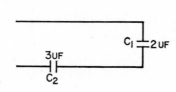

$$C_t = \frac{C_1 \times C_2}{C_1 + C_2}$$

$$= \frac{2 \times 3}{2 + 3}$$

$$= \frac{6}{5} = 1.2 \text{ mfd}$$

3. What is the total capacitance?

$$C_t = \frac{C_1 \times C_2}{C_1 + C_2}$$

$$= \frac{6 \times 12}{6 + 12}$$

$$= \frac{72}{18} = 4 \text{ mfd}$$

4. What is the total capacitance?

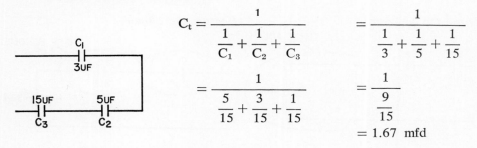

$$C_t = \cfrac{1}{\cfrac{1}{C_1} + \cfrac{1}{C_2} + \cfrac{1}{C_3}} = \cfrac{1}{\cfrac{1}{2} + \cfrac{1}{3} + \cfrac{1}{6}}$$

$$= \cfrac{1}{\cfrac{3}{6} + \cfrac{2}{6} + \cfrac{1}{6}} \qquad = \cfrac{1}{\cfrac{6}{6}}$$

$$= 1 \text{ mfd}$$

5. What is the total capacitance?

$$C_t = \cfrac{1}{\cfrac{1}{C_1} + \cfrac{1}{C_2} + \cfrac{1}{C_3}} = \cfrac{1}{\cfrac{1}{3} + \cfrac{1}{5} + \cfrac{1}{15}}$$

$$= \cfrac{1}{\cfrac{5}{15} + \cfrac{3}{15} + \cfrac{1}{15}} \qquad = \cfrac{1}{\cfrac{9}{15}}$$

$$= 1.67 \text{ mfd}$$

A Combination of Parallel and Series Capacitors

What is the total capacitance of this circuit?

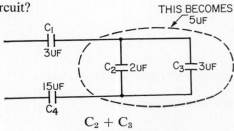

Add the two parallel capacitors.

$C_2 + C_3$

2 mfd + 3 mfd = 5 mfd

Redraw the circuit.

$$C_t = \cfrac{1}{\cfrac{1}{C_1} + \cfrac{1}{C_2} + \cfrac{1}{C_3}} = \cfrac{1}{\cfrac{1}{3} + \cfrac{1}{5} + \cfrac{1}{15}}$$

$$= \cfrac{1}{\cfrac{5}{15} + \cfrac{3}{15} + \cfrac{1}{15}} \qquad = \cfrac{1}{\cfrac{9}{15}}$$

$$= 1.67 \text{ mfd}$$

Treat it as a *series* circuit.

Word Problem

Assume you have two capacitors in series, each having a capacitance of 2 mfd. Further assume you have two capacitors in parallel with the first capacitors. Each of the parallel capacitors has a capacitance of 4 mfd. What is the total capacitance of the circuit?

Draw the problem: *Redraw the circuit:*

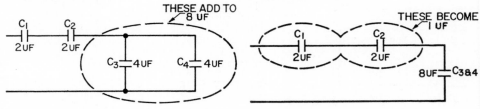

Formula:

$$C_t = \frac{C_{1 \text{ and } 2} \times C_{3 \text{ and } 4}}{C_{1 \text{ and } 2} + C_{3 \text{ and } 4}}$$

$$= \frac{1 \times 8}{1 + 8} = \frac{8}{9} = .89 \text{ mfd}$$

CAPACITORS AND WORK

An Interesting Fact

If a capacitor has no charge upon its plates it is said to be neutral. It has as many positive charges as negative charges.

Assume each plate of this capacitor has 4 positive and 4 negative charges.

If two positive charges are moved from plate *A* to plate *B* of the above capacitor, *B* will then have a total of six positive charges as compared with two charges on plate *A*. The difference, then, is 4 positive charges (*twice as many* as were moved from *A* to *B*).

From the above example it is apparent one can state an interesting fact regarding mathematics: *If two objects contain equal amounts of anything, and a quantity is transferred from one object to the other, the difference is always twice the amount transferred.*

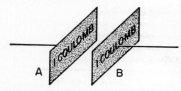

If $\frac{1}{2}$ coulomb is transferred from plate A to plate B, B will then have $1\frac{1}{2}$ coulombs or 1 coulomb more than A. Once again, this is twice as much as was transferred to B.

Moving 4 coulombs from one plate to another provides an 8 coulomb difference, *twice* the amount moved.

Moving 10 coulombs from one plate to another provides a 20 coulomb difference; *twice* the amount moved.

Another Important Way of Looking at the Same Concept

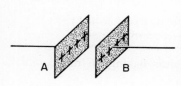

Again there is a capacitor with equal charges on both plates. If 4 charges are moved from A to B, B will have 8 charges. This is twice as many as were moved. *But A* lost only *one half* as many as B ends up having. The total amount of charge moved is one half the total remaining charge.

Thus, moving 4 coulombs from one plate to another provides an 8 coulomb difference — $\frac{4}{8}$ or $\frac{1}{2}$ Q is the total amount of charge.

Moving 10 coulombs from one plate to another provides a 20 coulomb difference — $\frac{10}{20}$ or $\frac{1}{2}$ Q is the total amount of charge moved.

Moving a charge requires work, just as it requires work to move *anything* from one place to another. You will remember the formula for work is $W = Q\,V$. But, in determining the work required *to charge a capacitor*, the formula must be modified to read: $W_C = (\frac{1}{2}\,Q) \times V$.

Can you understand why? Of course you can!

Recall the last problem: moving 10 coulombs from one plate to another provides a 20-coulomb charge on the second plate, *but* $\frac{1}{2}Q$ ($\frac{10}{20}$) is the total amount of charge actually moved. Hence the formula for the work involved in charging a capacitor is:

THE FORMULA

$$W_C = \frac{1}{2}\,Q\,V$$

What becomes of the work expended in moving a charge from one plate to another? It becomes *stored* in the capacitor in the form of energy. One might then correctly say the *work stored* in a capacitor is $W_C = \frac{1}{2}\,Q\,V$.

135

■ Problems

1. A certain amount of work must be expended in storing 60 millicoulombs at a potential of 100 volts. How much work will be required?

$$\textit{Formula: } W_C = \tfrac{1}{2} \, Q \, V$$
$$\textit{Substitute and solve: } W_C = \tfrac{1}{2} \, (60 \times 10^{-3}) \, (100)$$
$$= 3 \text{ joules}$$

2. A capacitor has stored 40 millicoulombs at a potential of 80 volts. How much work does this represent?

$$\textit{Formula: } W_C = \tfrac{1}{2} \, Q \, V$$
$$\textit{Substitute and solve: } W_C = \tfrac{1}{2} \, (40 \times 10^{-3}) \, (80)$$
$$= 1.6 \text{ joules}$$

3. How much energy is stored in a capacitor having 20 millicoulombs stored on its plates at a potential of 4 kilovolts (4 kv)?

$$\textit{Formula: } W_C = \tfrac{1}{2} \, Q \, V$$
$$\textit{Substitute and solve: } W_C = \tfrac{1}{2} \, (20 \times 10^{-3}) \, (4 \times 10^3)$$
$$= 40 \times 10^0 = 40 \text{ joules}$$

4. How much energy is stored in a 75 mfd capacitor having 76 millicoulombs at a potential of 500 volts?

$$\textit{Formula: } W_C = \tfrac{1}{2} \, Q \, V$$
$$\textit{Substitute and solve: } W_C = \tfrac{1}{2} \, (76 \times 10^{-3}) \, (500)$$
$$= 19 \text{ joules}$$

A Slightly Different Problem

How much energy is stored in a fully charged capacitor having 20 mfd at a potential of 200 volts?

Obviously you cannot use the formula $W_C = \tfrac{1}{2} Q V$ because you did not have Q given. It is necessary to solve for Q *before* solving for W!

Do you remember the formula for Q? You should! $Q = C \, V$. The problem could be worked this way:

Part one:

$$\textit{Formula: } Q = C \, V$$
$$\textit{Substitute and solve: } Q = (20 \times 10^{-6}) \, (200)$$
$$= 4{,}000 \times 10^{-6} \text{ or } 4 \times 10^{-3}$$
$$\text{or } 4 \text{ millicoulombs}$$

Part two:

$$\textit{Formula: } W_C = \tfrac{1}{2} \, Q \, V$$
$$\textit{Substitute and solve: } W_C = \tfrac{1}{2} \, (4 \times 10^{-3}) \, (200)$$
$$= .4 \text{ joule (final answer)}$$

Thus, if capacitance and voltage are known, work can be computed by first *solving for charge* (Q). *This is the* long *method.*

A Better Method — a Shortcut

Another method could also be used — a method which would require only *one formula* instead of two.

Analyze the two formulas for charge and work.

$$\text{Formula for Charge:} \quad Q = C\,V$$
$$\text{Formula for Work:} \quad W_C = \tfrac{1}{2}\,Q\,V$$

From the two formulas above it is easily seen that the formula for work *could be written:*

$$W_C = \tfrac{1}{2}\,(C\,V) \times V$$

or simply $W_C = \tfrac{1}{2}\,(C\,V)\,V$

This is the same as Q.

Since there are two V's, they could be combined to V^2 or $V \times V$.

The formula would then be: $W_C = \tfrac{1}{2}\,C\,V^2$.

Rework the last problem again using *one* formula instead of two.

■ Problem

How much energy is stored in a fully-charged capacitor having 20-mfd capacitance at a potential of 200 volts?

$$\text{Formula:} \quad W_C = \tfrac{1}{2}\,C\,V^2$$
$$\text{Substitute and solve:} \quad W_C = \tfrac{1}{2}\,(20 \times 10^{-6})\,(200)\,(200)$$
$$= .4 \text{ joule}$$

THE FORMULA

$$W_c = \tfrac{1}{2}\,C\,V^2$$

To be used in finding work when only capacitance and voltage are known.

■ Problem 1

An 80-mfd capacitor is charged by a 50-volt battery. How much work is accomplished? *Formula:* $W_C = \tfrac{1}{2}\,C\,V^2$

$$\text{Substitute and solve:} \quad W_C = \tfrac{1}{2}\,(80 \times 10^{-6})\,(50)\,(50)$$
$$= (40 \times 10^{-6})\,(25 \times 10^2)$$
$$= .1 \text{ joule}$$

■ Problem 2

A 500-mfd capacitor is charged by a 40-volt battery. How much work is accomplished? *Formula:* $W_C = \tfrac{1}{2}\,C\,V^2$

$$\text{Substitute and solve:} \quad W_C = \tfrac{1}{2}\,(500 \times 10^{-6})\,(40^2)$$
$$= (250 \times 10^{-6})\,(16 \times 10^2)$$
$$= .4 \text{ joule}$$

TIME AND CAPACITORS

For a further understanding of capacitors it is necessary to recall the unit dealing with time, charge, and current. You will remember the formula you worked with was

$$Q = I t$$

(Charge in coulombs) = (Amperes) × (Time in seconds)

If charge and amperage were known it would be possible to find time by changing the formula to:

$$t = \frac{Q}{I}$$

Using the Formula

A capacitor has 20×10^{-3} coulombs (.02) being stored on its plates by a 100-volt potential. A steady current of .1 ampere is flowing. How long will it take to charge the capacitor fully?

Formula: $t = \dfrac{Q}{I}$

Substitute and solve: $t = \dfrac{.02}{.1}$

$$= .2 \text{ seconds}$$

Assume for your next problem the charge was *not* given. Instead, the problem is:

A 200-mfd capacitor is being charged by a 100-volt source with a steady current of .1 ampere flowing. How long will it take to charge the capacitor fully?

Since the charge (Q) is not given, it will be necessary to solve for it.

Part one:

Formula: $Q = C V$

Substitute and solve: $Q = (200 \times 10^{-6}) (100)$

$$= 20 \times 10^{-3}$$

Part two:

Formula: $t = \dfrac{Q}{I}$

$$= \frac{20 \times 10^{-3}}{.1} = 200 \times 10^{-3}$$

$$= .2 \text{ seconds}$$

■ Problem

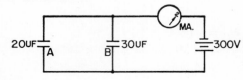

How long will it take to charge fully capacitors *A* and *B* if the current remains at 2 ma?

Part one:

$$Q = C\,V$$
$$= (50 \times 10^{-6})\,(300)$$
$$= 15 \times 10^{-3}$$

Part two:

$$t = \frac{Q}{I}$$
$$= \frac{15 \times 10^{-3}}{2 \times 10^{-3}} = 7.5 \text{ seconds}$$

(*Note:* 2 ma is the same as .002 amperes. or 2×10^{-3}.)

Remember These Facts

A. Capacitors in parallel *add*.

B. The *total capacitance* of capacitors in *series* will always be less than the smallest capacitor.

C. When solving for total capacitance in series use the following formulas:

$$C_t = \frac{C_1 \times C_2}{C_1 + C_2}$$

$$C_t = \frac{1}{\dfrac{1}{C_1} + \dfrac{1}{C_2} + \dfrac{1}{C_3} + \text{etc.}}$$

D. When solving for charge use this formula:

$$Q = C\,V$$

E. When solving for capacitance, use this formula:

$$C = \frac{Q}{V}$$

F. When solving for the time it takes to charge a capacitor fully, use this formula:

$$t = \frac{Q}{I}$$

G. When solving for work, when charge is known, use this formula:

$$W_C = \tfrac{1}{2}\,Q\,V$$

H. When solving for work when capacitance and voltage are known, use this formula:

$$W_C = \tfrac{1}{2}\,C\,V^2$$

How Resistance Affects Capacitor Charging Time

You will recall added resistance in a circuit results in less current flow if voltage is held constant.

On the other hand, the equation $t = \dfrac{Q}{I}$ clearly shows that time increases as current becomes less.

Thus: (1) Resistance decreases current flow. (2) A decrease in current flow results in an increase in time required to charge a capacitor.

Both of these concepts can be proven mathematically:

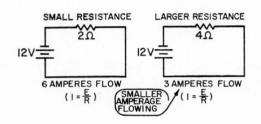

It takes 50 seconds to charge this capacitor to 50 coulombs with 1 ampere flowing.

$$t = \frac{Q}{I}$$

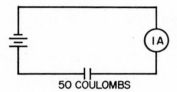

It takes 25 seconds to charge this capacitor to 50 coulombs with 2 amperes flowing.

$$t = \frac{Q}{I}$$

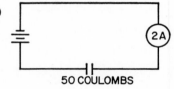

It will take longer to charge capacitor "A" than it will to charge capacitor "B."

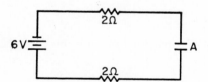 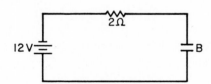

The more resistance placed in series with the capacitor, the longer it takes to charge it.

Time Constants

The amount of time required to charge a capacitor is a very important consideration when designing circuits for television, radio, oscilloscopes, and electronic test equipment.

It is always convenient to have some kind of standard for reference. In electronics, engineers and technicians often speak of *time constant.*

When resistance is multiplied times capacitance, the resultant answer is the time constant. It is the time required for a capacitor to charge to 63.2% of its full value.

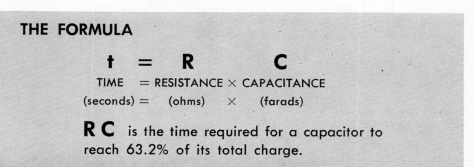

THE FORMULA

$$t = R \quad C$$

TIME = RESISTANCE × CAPACITANCE

(seconds) = (ohms) × (farads)

R C is the time required for a capacitor to reach 63.2% of its total charge.

The *R C* relationship may be expressed in graph form:

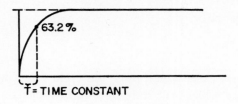

63.2%

T = TIME CONSTANT

■ Problems

1. How long will it take this capacitor to charge to 63.2% of its full value?

Formula: t = R C
Substitute and solve:

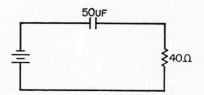

50UF

40Ω

$$t = (40) \ (50 \times 10^{-6})$$
$$= 2 \times 10^{-3} \ \text{or} \ 2 \ \text{milliseconds}$$

2. How long will it take this capacitor to charge to 63.2% of its full value?

Formula: t = R C
Answer: 6 milliseconds

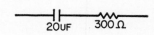

20UF   300Ω

3. How long will it take this capacitor to charge to 63.2% of its full value?

10K   50UF

Answer: 500 milliseconds
or .5 second

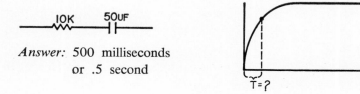

T = ?

4. Find the time constant.

> *Given:*   Resistance = 2 megohms
>   Capacitance = 20 microfarads
>   time constant = ?
>
> *Answer:* 40 seconds

5. Find the time constant.

> *Given:*   Resistance = 6×10^6 ohms
>   Capacitance = 20×10^{-6} farads
>   time constant = ?
>
> *Answer:* 120 seconds or 2 minutes

REMEMBER

As resistance increases it takes more time to charge a capacitor.

■ Summary

Capacitors, sometimes called condensers, are often found in electronic circuits. A capacitor is a device which will store an electrical charge, which is measured in coulombs. A capacitor which can store 1 coulomb of charge under a pressure of 1 volt is said to have a capacitance of 1 farad. Capacitance represents opposition to a change in voltage — it tends to hold down a rise in voltage, and it attempts to sustain a decline in voltage. The amount of charge a capacitor is able to store depends upon the applied voltage and the capacitance of the capacitor.

Capacitors connected in parallel *add* capacitance; capacitors connected in series will have a total capacitance less than the smallest capacitor in the circuit.

Resistance directly affects the time required to charge a capacitor. Resistance multiplied times capacitance results in a *time constant*. The time constant (sometimes referred to as the RC constant) represents the time required for a capacitor to reach 63.2% of its total charge. One must know how to calculate time constants in order to design many different kinds of electronic circuits.

REVIEW QUESTIONS

1. Briefly describe a *farad*.

2. A capacitor having a rating of 30 microfarads, with an applied voltage of 400 volts, will store how much charge (in coulombs)?

3. A capacitor rated at 20 microfarads and having 150 volts impressed upon it will store how many coulombs?

4. Three capacitors are connected in parallel. Each one has a rating of 40 mfd. What is the total capacitance?

5. Two capacitors are connected in parallel. One is 15 mfd and the other 10 mfd. What is the total capacitance?

6. Two capacitors are connected in series. One is 15 mfd and the other 20 mfd. What is the total capacitance?

7. Three capacitors are connected in series. They have the following ratings: 5 mfd, 10 mfd, 20 mfd. What is the total capacitance?

8. How much work will be expended in storing 50 millicoulombs at a potential of 100 volts?

9. How much work will be expended in storing 25 millicoulombs at 250 volts?

10. What will be the time constant of a circuit having a capacitor rated at 50 coulombs of charge?

11. What will be the time constant of a circuit having a capacitor rated at 20 mfd and a 3k ohm resistor?

12. What will be the time constant of a circuit having a resistor with the following color code: brown, black, yellow. It also contains a series capacitor valued at 100 microfarads.

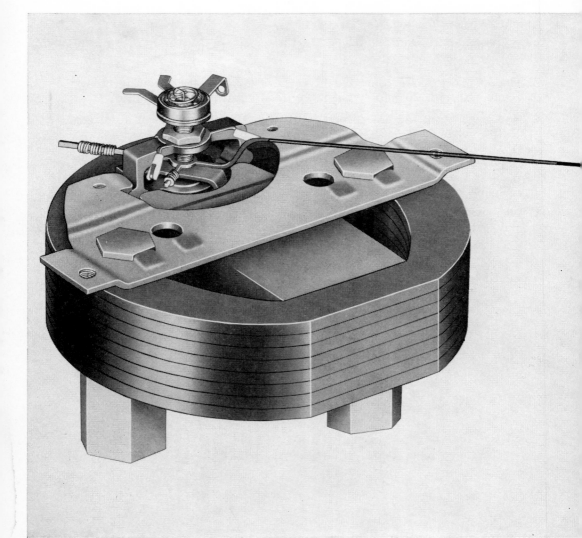

Unit 12

The modern concept of electronics would be completely nonexistent if it were not for meters. Ammeters, voltmeters, ohmmeters, wattmeters, meggers, multimeters, vacuum-tube voltmeters, and many hundreds of very specialized instruments are used everyday in all phases of the electronics industry. Fortunately, nearly all meters, regardless of their names or specialized uses, operate on the same principle, and are basically manufactured with the same kind of movement, or "innards."

The principle used is that of magnetic attraction and repulsion.

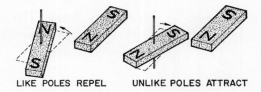

LIKE POLES REPEL   UNLIKE POLES ATTRACT

The magnets used are both permanent magnets and electromagnets.

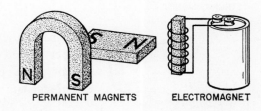

PERMANENT MAGNETS   ELECTROMAGNET

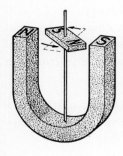

If two permanent magnets were used, like poles would repel and unlike poles would attract until *unlike* poles aligned themselves as shown in this drawing. A force would then be required to move them apart. The south pole of the rotating bar magnet would align itself with the north pole of the stationary horseshoe magnet, and vice versa.

145

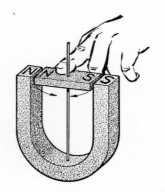

If one attempted to align *like poles,* he would find it would not work, because as soon as the finger pressure was released, the poles would again move apart.

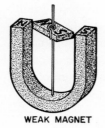

WEAK MAGNET

If a spring were added to limit the amount of travel, caused by the repelling action of like poles, a weak rotating bar magnet would not travel in as great an arc as that traveled by a *stronger* bar magnet. Compare the amount of travel of the two bar magnets which are mounted in the horseshoe magnets shown. The stronger magnet causes the bar magnet to move in a much larger arc away from the poles of the horseshoe magnet.

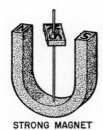

STRONG MAGNET

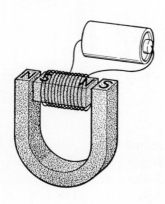

A meter uses a rotating magnet, and a permanent magnet shaped like a horseshoe. The rotating magnet cannot be a permanent magnet, but instead is an electromagnet.

Whenever an electric current travels through a wire, an electromagnetic field is produced. If the wire is wound into a tight coil the electromagnetic lines of force are concentrated, and the magnet becomes stronger. Winding the wire upon a soft iron core concentrates the lines of force even more, thus making a more "efficient" magnet.

The soft iron core upon which the windings are wound forms a north and a south pole, the positions of which depend upon the manner in which the windings are wound upon the core, and upon the direction of electron flow.

146

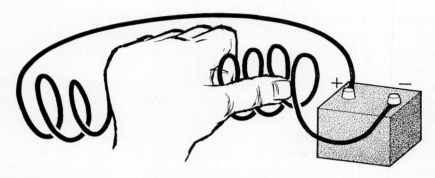

The *left-hand rule* can be used to determine the polarity of a coil of wire. If the coil is grasped with the left hand in such a manner that the fingers point in the direction of electron flow — from minus to plus — the thumb automatically points in the direction of the north pole.

Moving the Magnet

As current flows through a coil of wire a magnet is created. The greater the current flow, the more dense are the electromagnetic lines of flux. On the other hand, when no current flows the soft iron core retains no magnetism.

When the electromagnet is placed within the permanent magnetic field of a horseshoe magnet, and a spring is attached to the electromagnetic core, the movement for a meter has been created.

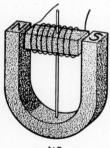
NO
CURRENT FLOWING

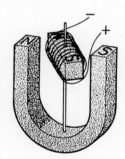
A SMALL
CURRENT FLOWING

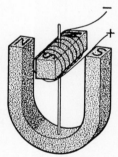
A GREATER
CURRENT FLOWING

The addition of a scale and a pointer provides a galvanometer — an ammeter which measures very small amounts of amperage.

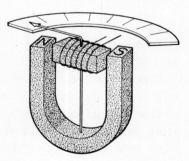

Obviously a method is needed for connecting the outside source of current to the coil wound upon the soft iron core. This is accomplished by placing a spring at the bottom of the iron core as well as at the top. Each spring is connected to a terminal.

The electrons from the source enter one terminal and leave from the other, hence one becomes a positive terminal and the other carries a negative sign.

The springs not only serve to return the needle to zero when no current flows but they also serve as conductors over which the current flows.

The bottom spring is wound in a direction opposite to the top spring, thus compensating for changes in temperature which might otherwise affect the meter's accuracy. The springs are usually made of phosphor bronze, a metal which contains the necessary "springlike" characteristics, and yet is a good electrical conductor.

In the real meter the winding of wire is not wound directly upon the iron core, but rather upon a very light rectangular aluminum frame which is free to rotate *around* the iron core. By using a very light metal, such as aluminum, the meter is much more sensitive. Using aluminum also helps to create a damping action of the movement, permitting the needle to return to zero relatively slowly when current is removed, rather than striking the zero stop pin with too great a force.

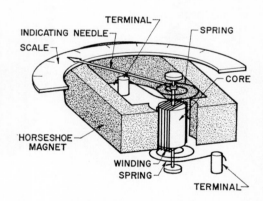

The meter movement is sometimes referred to as the *D'Arsonval* movement. It is named after Arsene d'Arsonval, the man who designed the galvanometer in 1882.

How can *one* meter movement serve so many different purposes?

It is true that nearly *all* meters, including voltmeters, ohmmeters, ammeters, and others, are really galvanometers — *ammeters* that measure very small currents, usually in the range of milliamperes . . . thousandths of one ampere. The *basic movement* is modified to serve many different purposes.

Ammeters

Modifying the basic movement is a simple matter for making an ammeter which can measure greater amperages than the galvanometer alone could handle.

Shunt resistors are added to the basic movement. These are simply low-resistance resistors which are connected in parallel with the movement's coil. A parallel connection is sometimes called a "shunt" connection.

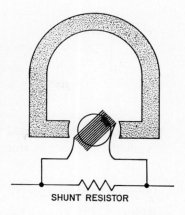

SHUNT RESISTOR

If an ammeter is connected in parallel with the circuit, the meter will probably be burned out. Instead, it must be connected in series as shown below.

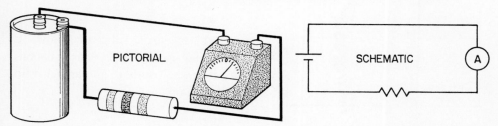

PICTORIAL

SCHEMATIC   Ⓐ

The circuit *must be broken* and the ammeter connected *in series* with the circuit.

Voltmeters

The basic galvanometer movement may be modified to construct a voltmeter by adding *multiplier resistors* in *series* with the meter movement.

The circuit being tested should be connected to the positive and negative terminals. Note that the multiplier resistor is connected in *series* with the meter movement. The larger the multiplier resistor, the higher is the voltage which can be measured.

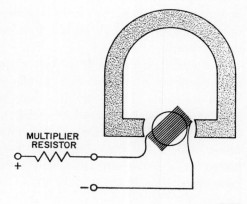

MULTIPLIER
RESISTOR

+

THE RULE

A voltmeter must ALWAYS be connected in PARALLEL with the circuit being tested, or in parallel with the resistance across which the voltage drop is measured.

If a voltmeter is connected in series with the circuit being tested, the indication will undoubtedly be in error.

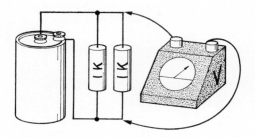

Instead, it must be connected in *parallel* as shown in the pictorial drawing to the left.

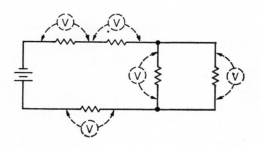

The schematic diagram shows a voltmeter moved to various locations to secure a reading in parallel with the resistors.

Ohmmeters

Ohmmeters basically are of two types. The first is a series type meter. In a series type ohmmeter a battery is connected in series with the movement.

The circuit is designed in such a manner that whenever a jumper wire is placed between terminals *A* and *B,* the meter needle indicates full scale. Instead of being graduated in volts, the scale is graduated in ohms, and a full-scale reading is *not* calibrated as a maximum value, but rather as *zero* ohms.

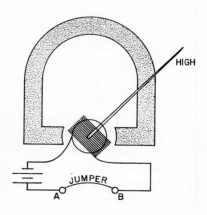

150

One can readily see that as the jumper is replaced with a resistor, less current flows through the meter, because a certain voltage drop occurs across the unknown resistor. The greater the resistance of the unknown resistor, the greater is the voltage dropped across it, and the less is the current through the coil of the meter. Consequently, the *higher* the ohms rating of the resistor, the less farther the needle of the meter is deflected.

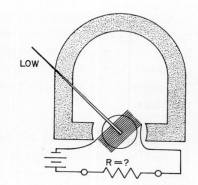

Because of the manner in which the meter scale is calibrated, a smaller meter current (caused by a higher resistance) is calibrated on the scale as a higher ohms value.

All ohmmeters have built-in batteries which serve as the power source.

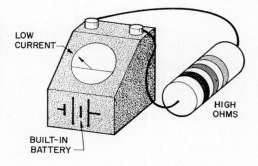

The second type of ohmmeter is the *shunt ohmmeter* which permits very *low* resistances to be measured accurately.

THE RULE

It is absolutely essential that NO VOLTAGE be connected to an ohmmeter, or permanent damage will surely result.

Multirange Meters and Their Circuits

It is many times inconvenient to have separate meters for measuring volts, ohms, and amperes. To overcome this difficulty one meter movement is used, and circuits are designed which permit the one movement to serve several different purposes. The face of the meter contains many scales, and the entire meter is called a *multirange meter*.

A multirange ammeter can be constructed by switching different resistors into a shunt circuit, or by plugging test leads into different shunt jacks. The schematic to the right represents the latter.

A multirange voltmeter can be constructed by switching different multiplier resistors into series circuits, or by plugging test leads into different series jacks.

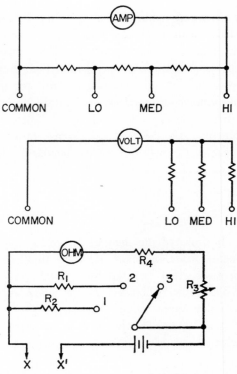

A multirange series ohmmeter can be constructed with switches, or by providing jacks which connect fixed resistors of different values into the circuit.

Look at the schematic to the right. With the switch in position *3*, the ohmmeter is connected as a purely series circuit on the highest range. In position *2*, R_1 is connected in *parallel* with the meter, which changes the series resistance of the circuit and permits accurate measurement of a lower value resistor at points X and X'. Switching to position *1* provides an even lower ohms range for measuring still smaller resistances. R_3 is a variable resistor which permits adjusting the circuit for varying voltages the battery delivers as it ages. R_4 is a fixed resistor which prevents excess current from flowing and burning out the meter.

A.C. Meters

Thus far only direct current — d.c. — meters have been discussed. The moving-coil galvanometer is a direct-current instrument which cannot possibly work for alternating current — a.c. — unless the circuit is modified. Since the moving-coil galvanometer can handle *only* d.c. it is obvious that alternating current must somehow be changed to direct current prior to being connected to the meter movement. The change is accomplished by connecting a *rectifier* into the circuit.

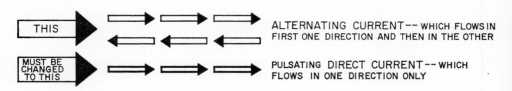

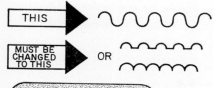

THE SYMBOL FOR A.C.

THE SYMBOL FOR PULSATING D.C.
(HALF - WAVE)

THE SYMBOL FOR PULSATING D.C.
(FULL-WAVE)

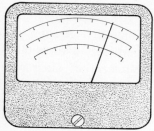

The meter measures the *average* of the pulsations.

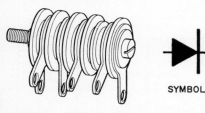

SYMBOL

A rectifier is an electrical component which changes a.c. to d.c. Meter rectifiers have traditionally been made of one or more sections of copper oxide. Selenium rectifiers have also been used, but to a much more limited extent. With the advancements being made in semiconductor materials, it is anticipated that germanium and silicon will play an ever-increasing role in meter rectification.

A rectifier offers a low resistance to the flow of current in one direction, but a very high resistance to the flow of current in the opposite direction. Thus, it permits current to flow one way, but not in the other. This is known as *rectification*, or the changing of a.c. to d.c.

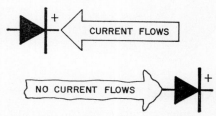

A.c. meters employing the moving-coil galvanometer use one or more rectifiers for purposes of rectification.

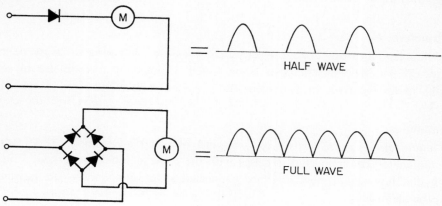

HALF WAVE

FULL WAVE

The use of a single rectifier produces what is known as *half-wave* rectification. Two or four rectifiers produce *full-wave* rectification. Full-wave rectification can more easily be made to closely resemble pure direct current, such as that which is provided by a battery.

The Multimeter

The multimeter combines all of the features of the multirange voltmeter, ammeter, and ohmmeter. Oftentimes resistors serve dual purposes, and rectifiers are added to multimeters in order to permit the measurement of alternating current as well as direct current, at various voltages.

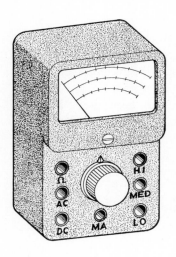
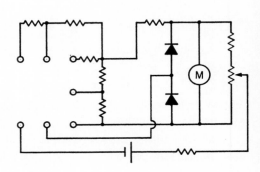

Ammeters

Ammeters are used for measuring amperage — electrical current. An ammeter must be connected in *series* with the circuit being tested. Connecting an ammeter in parallel results in burnout.

Voltmeters

Voltmeters measure voltage — electrical pressure. A voltmeter must be connected in parallel with the load being tested. Connecting a voltmeter in series results in an incorrect measurement.

Ohmmeters

Ohmmeters measure resistance — a kind of electrical friction. The leads of the ohmmeter are connected in series with the resistance being checked. Voltage, no matter how small, must *never* be connected to an ohmmeter — the movement may be damaged.

REVIEW QUESTIONS

1. The left-hand rule can be used to determine the polarity of a coil of wire. When the fingers of the left hand point in the direction of _____ _____, from minus to plus, the thumb points in the direction of the _____ pole.

2. Shunt resistors are used when extending the range of a/an _____.

3. Multiplier resistors are used when extending the range of a/an _____.

4. Resistors connected in series with a meter movement are the same as _____ resistors.

5. Resistors connected in parallel with a meter movement are the same as _____ resistors.

6. Ammeters must always be connected in _____ with the circuit being tested.

7. Voltmeters must always be connected in _____ with the circuit being tested.

8. A voltage, no matter how small, may *never* be connected to a/an _____.

9. Ammeters, voltmeters, and ohmmeters which can measure more than one range of values are known as _____ meters.

10. Galvanometer movements can measure either a.c. or d.c. providing a _____ is used.

11. Meter rectifiers have very often been constructed using one or more sections of _____ _____.

12. Rectifiers change _____ _____ to _____ _____.

13. The use of a single rectifier can produce only _____-wave rectification.

14. The use of four rectifiers can produce _____-wave rectification.

15. A single meter which can measure amperage, voltage, and resistance at many different values, and which can measure either a.c. or d.c. is known as a _____.

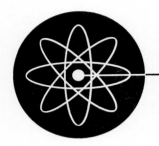

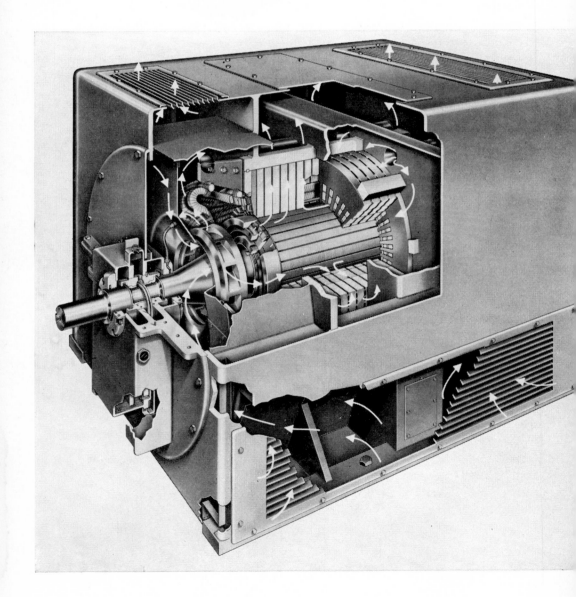

Unit 13

GENERATORS AND MOTORS

Understanding the theory and operation of generators and motors helps one more fully comprehend direct and alternating current. In this unit generators and motors are treated separately under the two broad classifications of d.c. and a.c. Since both generators and motors depend upon magnetism, this particular phenomenon is reviewed as it directly relates to this new unit.

Magnetism

Natural magnets are found in the earth, and are called *magnetite* or *lodestone*. It is a type of ore found throughout the world, but which is especially abundant in Asia Minor.

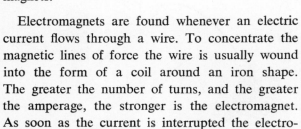

Artificial magnets may be either permanent or temporary magnets. In either case they represent a ferrous metal, or an alloy of metals which are magnetized by being placed in another magnetic field of force. Magnets are manufactured in many shapes and sizes, the most common of which are bar magnets and horseshoe magnets.

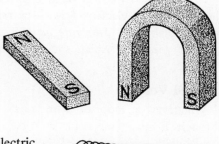

Electromagnets are found whenever an electric current flows through a wire. To concentrate the magnetic lines of force the wire is usually wound into the form of a coil around an iron shape. The greater the number of turns, and the greater the amperage, the stronger is the electromagnet. As soon as the current is interrupted the electromagnetism disappears.

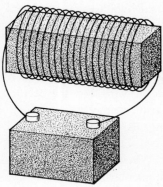

Every magnet has a magnetic field of force — thousands of invisible magnetic lines. These invisible lines of force, or magnetic field of flux, leave the north pole of the magnet, and enter the south pole.

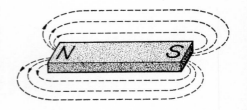

The stronger the magnet, the greater are the number of lines of flux, and the more concentrated they are. It does not matter whether a magnet is the artificial type or an electromagnet, lines of flux always are present. The north pole of an electromagnet can be determined by using the *left-hand rule*.

Left-Hand Rule

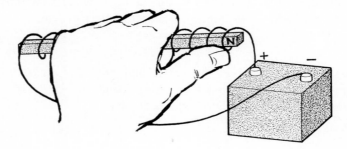

If one places his left hand over the coil of wire, with the fingers pointing in the direction of electron flow — current flow — the thumb points in the direction of the north pole. *This rule assumes that current flows from minus to plus.* It is an important rule which should be remembered.

Induced Voltage

Whenever a loop of wire cuts through a magnetic field, a very small voltage is produced in the loop of wire, and a tiny current flows. It is then said that a voltage is *induced* into the loop of wire. When a galvanometer is connected to the wire loop the needle momentarily swings to one side, indicating the induced voltage.

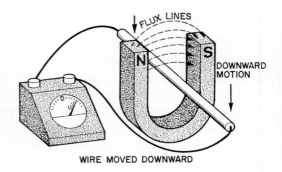

WIRE MOVED DOWNWARD

When the loop of wire is moved *upward* in this magnetic field the needle again momentarily swings to one side, but *in the opposite direction* from that shown in the preceding example. The stronger the magnet, the greater is the movement of the needle, indicating a greater induced voltage. If the wire loop is moved *quickly* through the lines of flux, the induced voltage is greater than it would be if the loop were moved slowly.

Moving the wire loop *parallel* to the lines of flux results in no induced voltage whatsoever. The loop must *cut across* the lines of force, and the heavier the concentration of flux lines, the greater is the induced voltage.

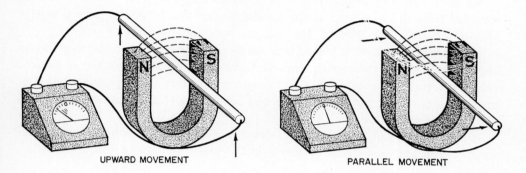

UPWARD MOVEMENT   PARALLEL MOVEMENT

Of course it does not matter whether the wire loop is moved and the magnet held stationary, or the loop held steady and the magnet moved. So long as the lines of flux cut, or are cut by, a wire, a voltage is induced.

It is also true that more voltage is induced if several loops of wire are used rather than one loop. The amount of voltage induced is directly proportional to the number of loops of wire.

THE RULE

If ONE loop of wire passes through 100,000,000 (10^8) lines of force in one second of time, one volt is induced.

It is interesting to see what happens when an electromagnet is used instead of a permanent magnet. Both permanent magnet and electromagnet function exactly alike *provided that the voltage source* which connects to the electromagnet *maintains a constant voltage. However,* a varying voltage produces a very interesting effect.

To understand the latter, note what happens when a varying voltage passes through a wire conductor. In the diagrams shown on page 160, the voltage source is not shown, and the wire appears not to be connected; this was done in order to simplify the drawing. The reader must mentally imagine a voltage source connected to the wire conductors shown.

WIRE

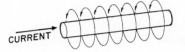
CURRENT

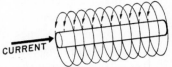
CURRENT

NO VOLTAGE APPLIED
NO MAGNETIC
LINES EXIST

A SMALL VOLTAGE APPLIED
WEAK MAGNETIC
LINES APPEAR

A HIGHER APPLIED VOLTAGE
PRODUCES STRONGER
MAGNETIC LINES OF FLUX

When a *pulsating* direct current is applied, magnetic lines of force expand outward from the wire loop as the applied voltage builds. As the source voltage dies down again, the lines of flux collapse back into the wire.

If a second wire loop is placed in a stationary position next to the loop having the expanding and contracting lines of force (flux lines), a voltage is *induced* into the second wire. Why? For the simple reason that the expanding and contracting lines of flux *cut across* the second conductor. This concept was explained on the preceding page.

It is important to remember this concept when dealing with generators and motors. The idea will again be useful in the unit dealing with transformers.

When no current flows in the first — primary — wire, there can be no magnetic lines of flux. With no flux lines cutting across the second — secondary — wire, no voltage can be induced into it.

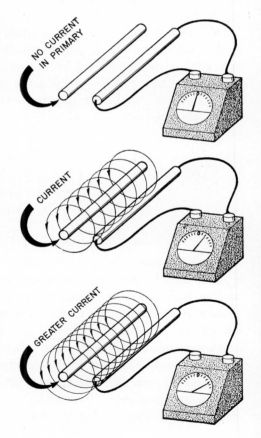

As current begins to flow, magnetic lines of flux extend outward and cut across the secondary. A voltage is induced into the secondary, and the voltmeter begins to register that rising voltage.

As the current increases in intensity in the primary wire the magnetic lines of flux become greater. A higher voltage is induced into the secondary. The greater voltage is indicated by the voltmeter.

As current begins to decrease in the primary, the magnetic lines of flux collapse back into that wire. When this happens, the lines of flux sweep *back* across the secondary. Because of this backward sweep of the flux lines the voltage which is induced is the *reverse* of that voltage originally induced.

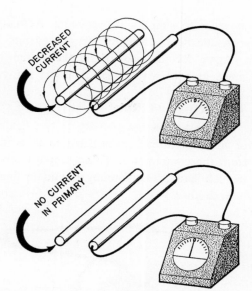

When the current in the primary ceases entirely the flux lines die out just as they do in any electromagnet. Again the voltmeter registers a zero reading.

REMEMBER

When a varying voltage is connected to one wire, or a group of wires — called a "primary" — the resulting expanding and collapsing lines of flux induce a voltage into another wire, or group of wires, which are placed parallel to the primary. The second wire is called a "secondary."

NEITHER PRIMARY NOR SECONDARY MOVE, but the lines of flux do move, and they do cut across the secondary from the primary. The result is a voltage which is induced into the secondary.

DIRECT-CURRENT GENERATORS

No matter how complex a generator may appear to be, it is fundamentally a simple d.c. device consisting of a magnetic field, an armature, a commutator, and brushes.

The magnetic field, either permanent or electromagnetic, provides the necessary field of force with its lines of flux. The armature consists of turns of wire which turn and cut through the flux lines, thus inducing a voltage into itself. The commutator acts as a switching device which provides direct current rather than alternating current, and the brushes pick off the voltage and supply the load so that an amperage may flow.

In the drawings which follow, the field is illustrated as a permanent magnet in order to simplify the drawing. Actually, almost all generators use an electromagnetic field served by a direct current source known as the "exciter."

Again for the sake of simplicity, the armature in the drawings is shown as a single loop of wire rather than the many turns found in a true-to-life generator.

The Left-Hand Rule

If one knows the polarity of the field's magnet, and the direction of rotation of the armature, it is possible to determine the direction of the flow of current from the commutator. To accomplish this one uses two fingers and the thumb of the left hand. The forefinger, middle finger, and thumb should all be at 90° to one another.

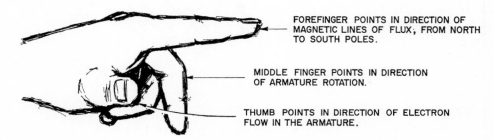

FOREFINGER POINTS IN DIRECTION OF MAGNETIC LINES OF FLUX; FROM NORTH TO SOUTH POLES.

MIDDLE FINGER POINTS IN DIRECTION OF ARMATURE ROTATION.

THUMB POINTS IN DIRECTION OF ELECTRON FLOW IN THE ARMATURE.

It is essential to remember this rule, and to know how to apply it in order to understand the generation of direct current as contrasted with alternating current. Memorize the rule, and apply it to the drawing below.

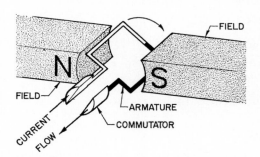

FIELD

FIELD

ARMATURE

COMMUTATOR

CURRENT FLOW

Note the black half of the loop. Use the left-hand rule and follow the rotation of the loop clockwise. As the black half of the loop moves downward (middle finger), and the magnetic lines of flux go from north to south (forefinger), the direction of the flow of current is *out from* the black half of the loop.

One can likewise determine the flow of current in the white half of the loop, simply by turning the hand half over, with the middle finger pointing upward. The flow of current in the white half goes *into* the loop.

If one mentally "turns" the loop of wire clockwise, and keeps track of *either* the black or the white half of the loop, using the left-hand rule, it is readily seen that the current flows in *one* direction only. *The flow of current does not change direction at any time.*

It does, however, build from zero voltage, rise to a maximum, then declines to zero again, rises to maximum once more, and on and on and on.

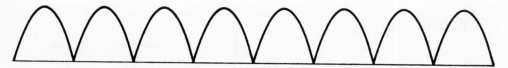

PULSATING DIRECT CURRENT

It is not difficult to understand how this happens if one recalls the information already learned. It will be remembered that in order to generate (induce) a voltage into a loop of wire, that wire must be actually *cutting* magnetic lines of force. When the loop of wire is running *parallel* to the lines of flux no voltage is induced, and the line on the voltage graph is on the *zero* voltage line.

As the loop of wire continues to turn, more and more lines of flux are cut per unit time. As the loop passes the center point of the magnetic field, it is perpendicular to the flux lines, and at that point the loop is cutting the maximum number of lines per unit of time. It is at that point that maximum voltage is generated. The two drawings which follow illustrate both the "no voltage," and the "maximum voltage" points.

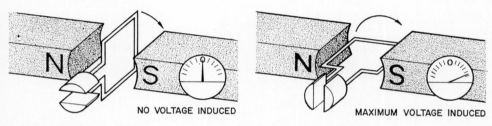

NO VOLTAGE INDUCED   MAXIMUM VOLTAGE INDUCED

When illustrated in graph form the direct current pulsations, and the positions of the armature loop appear as shown below. Note that the meter needle *never* moves to the left of the zero voltage mark on the meter — if it did, it would indicate a change in direction of current flow from the commutator, and one would then no longer have direct current!

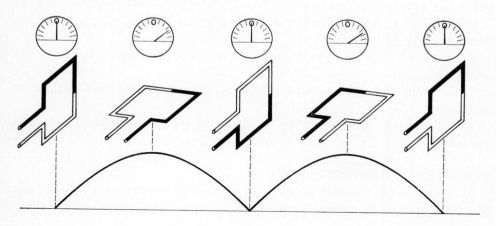

The commutator of a direct current generator serves as a switch permitting the induced current to flow in ONE DIRECTION ONLY.

The simplified drawings shown thus far do not illustrate the generator as it actually appears. The illustration shown below more nearly depicts the machine as it really is. Notice that the commutator is not merely two halves of a circle, but rather a series of segments, each of which connects to a winding on the armature. The field is not a permanent magnet, but rather windings of wire wound upon an iron core which is made up of laminated iron. When an electric current passes through the field winding, an electromagnet is created. As the armature turns in this magnetic field a voltage is induced into the armature's windings. The voltage is picked off from the commutator by means of the brushes.

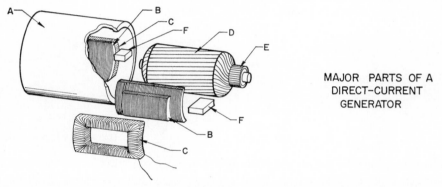

MAJOR PARTS OF A
DIRECT–CURRENT
GENERATOR

The *generator housing* (*A*) is simply a steel shell in which the major parts are housed.

Laminated iron core field pole (*B*) concentrates the magnetic lines of force which are produced by the field winding *C*.

Field coil (*C*). An electric current is fed into this winding (*C*) producing an electromagnetic field of flux.

Armature (*D*) turns inside of the field's magnetic flux, and a voltage is induced within the windings of the armature.

Commutator (*E*). The induced voltage of the armature is connected to the commutator.

The *brushes* (*F*) pick off the voltage from the commutator and connect it to the load.

THE DIRECT-CURRENT MOTOR

At this point the principle of operation of the direct-current motor should not be entirely new to the reader. Many of the concepts learned about direct-current generators can be directly applied to the motor. It is a matter of fact that many d.c. motors can be converted to d.c. generators with very minor modification.

The galvanometer studied in Unit 12 also operates on the same principle as the d.c. motor. If a voltage was connected to the coil (armature) of the galvanometer, and if the coil was designed to turn throughout a 360° range, it would indeed be a simple motor.

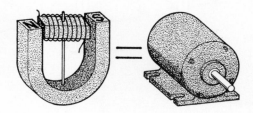

Many of the same illustrations which were used for the generator can also be used for the motor, but instead of picking a voltage *off* from the commutator, a voltage is fed *into* the commutator from a direct-current source. The armature, which is connected to the commutator, then becomes an electromagnet with a north and a south pole. Because of the switching arrangement mentioned in connection with generators, the polarity changes as the armature rotates. If the polarity did not change, the armature would rotate only to that position where unlike poles would be adjacent to one another. At that point they would "lock in" and refuse to turn any farther.

In diagram *A* below the north pole of the armature is in the upward position. Since like poles repel, and unlike poles attract, the north pole of the armature is repelled by the north pole of the field. At the same time the south field pole attracts the armature's north pole.

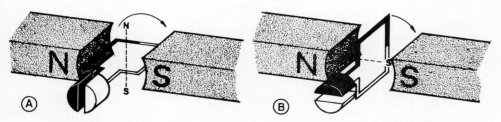

In diagram *B* in the drawing above the armature's polarity has changed due to the switching action of the commutator. The polarity of the field remains unchanged. Now the south pole of the field repels the south pole of the armature, while the north pole of the field repels the armature's north pole.

It should be remembered that while like poles are repelling one another, unlike poles are attracting.

It is possible to determine the direction of rotation of an armature by using the thumb, forefinger, and middle finger of the right hand.

Although the illustration indicates a permanent magnet for a field, actual motors use electromagnets which function in the exact same manner. The armature, which is pictured as a single wire loop, is actually made of many turns of wire wound on a cylindrical form.

Reversing Direction of Rotation

The direction of rotation of a motor's armature can be changed by reversing the leads to *either* the armature or the field winding. Reversing the leads to *both* causes the motor to run in the same direction as it did originally.

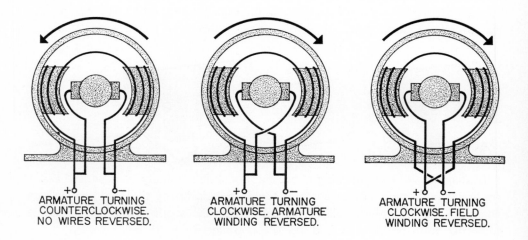

ARMATURE TURNING COUNTERCLOCKWISE. NO WIRES REVERSED.

ARMATURE TURNING CLOCKWISE. ARMATURE WINDING REVERSED.

ARMATURE TURNING CLOCKWISE. FIELD WINDING REVERSED.

Counter Electromotive Force (C.E.M.F.)

Many persons have noticed that a motor draws more current when first starting than it does after attaining its full running speed. This is very apparent when lights dim as a motor is first turned on, and then return to normal brilliance as soon as the motor comes up to full speed. This is an indication that the motor requires more current when starting than it does after attaining its rated revolutions per minute.

If one thinks about this phenomenon it is easily understood from the facts already studied. As the armature first begins to turn the full amount of source voltage is used, but as the armature revolves and gains speed, it partially acts as a generator. And why should it not act so? After all, the same conditions are present as were found in the generator: an armature turns in the presence of a magnetic field, and produces a voltage.

The voltage induced by the turning armature is *opposite* to the outside source voltage being fed into the motor. The voltage actually used by the motor is the difference between the outside source voltage and the opposing induced voltage. When the armature comes up to full speed the back voltage is at its greatest value, and the used voltage is at its minimum. The induced back voltage is often referred to as *counter electromotive force,* or simply as c.e.m.f. Forward current is thus cut to a very low figure, making the motor an unusually efficient device.

Speed Control

The speed of a direct current motor may be changed by changing the voltage applied to either the field winding or the armature winding. Obviously this can be accomplished by varying the *source* voltage, but that is not a practical method when one is dealing with fixed source voltages. It is much easier to place a variable resistor in series with the armature or field winding. Such a resistor causes a varying voltage drop to occur across that resistance, with a resulting varying voltage applied to the motor. Sewing machines often incorporate this kind of speed control.

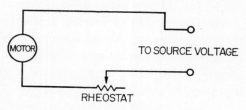

Specialized Windings

Connecting the field winding and armature winding in special ways provides different motor operating characteristics.

Shunt-Wired Motors

A motor which has its armature and field connected in parallel (*shunt*) is called a *constant-speed motor.* A motor thus wound is said to have no more than a 10 percent variation in speed from a no-load to a full-load condition. This is very desirable in applications demanding steady speed.

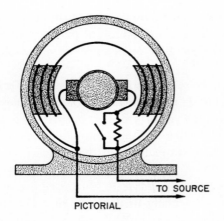

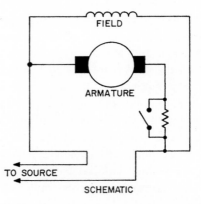

FIELD

ARMATURE

TO SOURCE

TO SOURCE

PICTORIAL

SCHEMATIC

As the load increases the motor tends to slow down, thus reducing the c.e.m.f. which in turn depends upon speed *and* a constant field strength. The reduced c.e.m.f. results in a greater current flow to the armature which in turn results in an increased torque needed to carry the increase in load.

As a load decreases the motor tends to speed up, thus increasing the c.e.m.f. and reducing the armature current, which in turn results in a decrease in torque or turning force.

One can readily see that as the load changes, the speed *tends* to change, but *only* until an electrical balance is met, at which point the speed levels off and remains constant. Unfortunately the shunt motor does not have a high starting torque for starting heavy loads. Instead its advantage lies in its constant speed.

Shunt-wired motors employ a resistance in series with the armature to limit the current drawn. As the motor builds up sufficient speed to produce enough *counter electromotive force,* and the danger of burning out the armature is no longer present, the starting resistor is effectively "taken out" of the circuit by bypassing it with a shorting switch.

REMEMBER

Shunt wired motors have excellent self regulation of speed, but relatively poor starting torque.

Series-Wired Motors

A motor which has its armature and field connected in series has the ability to start very heavy loads. It is said to have a high starting torque, such as that needed in many industrial applications.

In this motor the field winding consists of a few turns of heavy wire. As the load increases the motor slows down, decreasing the counter electromotive force.

With a decreased counter electromotive force, the current increases and thus furnishes the needed greater torque or turning force.

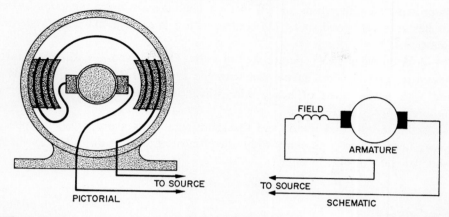

PICTORIAL

SCHEMATIC

The motor runs slowly when heavily loaded, and very fast with light loads. It is a fact that a series-wired motor can literally run so fast with no load that it flies apart and explodes. A series motor must therefore always have a load applied, even though the load be nothing more than a pulley.

The series motor is a variable-speed motor, its speed changing considerably with a change in load. Cranes, hoists, and electric trains use series motors because of their high starting torque, and because constant speed is not a necessarily desirable characteristic in that kind of equipment.

REMEMBER

Series wired motors have a high starting torque, but poor speed regulation.

Compound-Wired Motors

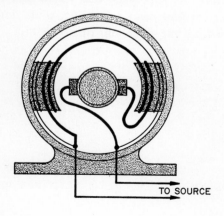

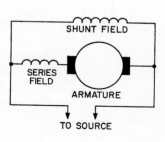

The compound-wired motor incorporates features found in both the series- and shunt-wired motors. Although the combined features must necessarily be a compromise, and therefore limited in their characteristics, the compound-wired motor has relatively good speed self-control with a fairly high starting torque and acceleration.

The field contains two separate sets of coils. One is wound with many turns of fine wire, and is wired in parallel with the armature. The second winding is wound with a few turns of heavy wire which is connected in series with the armature.

While the series-wired motor and the shunt-wired motor are excellent special-purpose motors, the compound-wired direct-current device may be considered a good general purpose machine.

REMEMBER

The compound motor is a compromise between the series and shunt motors. It provides the high starting torque of the former, and the speed control of the latter.

THE ALTERNATING-CURRENT GENERATOR

Alternating-current generators differ from direct-current generators in that the a.c. device has slip rings instead of a commutator. The slip rings permit the current to reverse direction, thus permitting it to flow first in one direction and then in another. The d.c. generator commutator, on the other hand, acts as a switch restricting the current flow to one direction only.

If one were to use the left-hand rule, with the forefinger pointing in the direction of the magnetic lines of flux from north to south, the middle finger pointing in the direction of armature movement, and the thumb pointing in the direction of current flow into and out from the slip rings, one would find that during 180° of travel of the armature current flows *into* a slip ring, while during the next 180° of travel current flows *out* from the same slip ring.

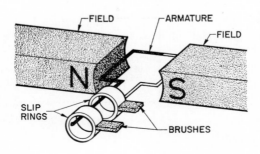

THE A.C. GENERATOR

Although it is difficult to visualize this current reversal when looking at the confines of a two-dimensional textbook page, the phenomenon becomes readily understood if one shapes a piece of wire as shown in the illustration and rotates it slowly throughout a full 360° of travel.

As the armature rotates the voltage builds from zero, to peak voltage, and back to zero in one direction. It then builds from zero to peak to zero in the opposite direction. This can be diagramed as shown below.

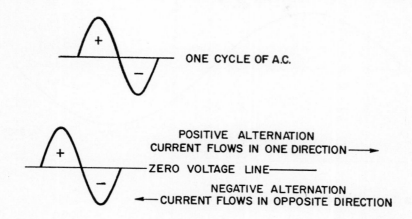

That part above the zero-voltage line represents a voltage or current in one direction, and is labeled with a positive symbol. That part of the diagram below the zero-voltage line represents a voltage or current in the opposite direction, and it is labeled with a negative symbol. Each half of the wave form is called an *alternation,* and each half represents 180° travel of the armature. Putting both halves together forms 360° of rotation, thus completing one full revolution of the armature.

Two alternations equal one cycle. One cycle forms what is known, mathematically, as a *sine wave.*

When illustrated in graph form the alternating-current sine wave, the position of the armature loop, and the galvanometer needle appear as shown in the illustration above. Note that the meter's needle moves both to the right and to the left of the zero mark, thus indicating a flow of current in *two* directions.

If the complete cycle — two alternations — takes place in the span of one second of time, it is said that the generated voltage has a *frequency* of 1 cycle per second. One c.p.s. would not be a very practical alternating current. *Sixty cycles per second is a very practical, and a very common frequency.* It is the frequency almost universally found supplied by electric light and power companies for industrial and home use. There is little doubt that when a homeowner plugs in an appliance to an outlet, he is using 110 to 120 volts, 60 cycles per second, alternating current.

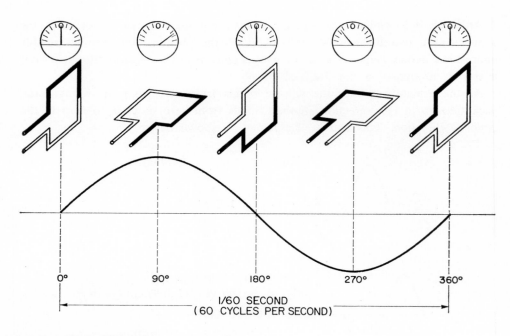

0°   90°   180°   270°   360°

1/60 SECOND
(60 CYCLES PER SECOND)

Why a Sine Wave?

The generated wave form, with its associated generator, is shown below. Notice how the 360° of the cylindrical armature is transposed to the sine wave.

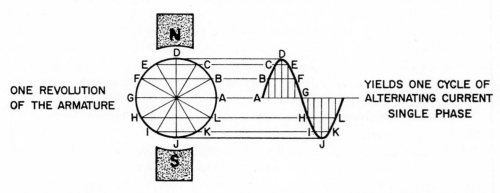

ONE REVOLUTION OF THE ARMATURE

YIELDS ONE CYCLE OF ALTERNATING CURRENT SINGLE PHASE

Take particular note of the *two* field poles, a *north* and a *south* pole. Two single poles, and one revolution of the armature provide *single-phase* current. Single-phase current is readily recognized because only a single sine wave is produced from one complete revolution of the armature. It is that current with which everyone is most familiar because it is the type supplied to homes. It is also the kind of alternating current most often seen in graph form, and it is the type most often discussed in textbooks.

Two- and three-phase alternating current generators will be discussed next. Of the two, three-phase is by far the more important.

Two-Phase A.C. Generator

A two-phase generator has two single-phase windings equidistantly spaced around the rotor. Being spaced in this manner, the alternating voltage induced into one winding is 90° out of phase with the voltage induced into the second winding. One winding is thus being cut by maximum flux while the other has no flux. The two windings are physically separated from one another, but are electrically "connected."

The schematic diagram below illustrates such a two-phase generator. For purposes of clarity the illustration shows a permanent magnet as the armature. In construction of *this kind,* the load voltage is picked off from the *field* winding. Although a generator constructed in this manner works on exactly the same principle as the more conventional one having a wound wire armature, most generators are the latter type because greater voltages and amperages can be obtained.

Generators having the more conventionally wound armature have the load voltage picked off from the armature rather than the field. By feeding a direct current into the field winding, the field serves as the electromagnet with its radiating lines of flux. One can understand that as the armature turns through the magnetic flux of the field, a voltage is generated in the moving armature.

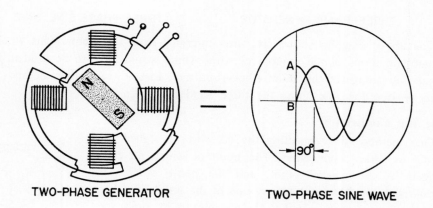

TWO-PHASE GENERATOR   TWO-PHASE SINE WAVE

Two-Phase Wave Form

The generated wave form supplied by the two-phase generator is illustrated above. As the armature rotates, its flux cuts through the windings. Sine wave *A* is that generated by one winding, while *B* is generated by the second. When *A* is at maximum voltage, *B* is at minimum, and *B* is therefore 90° out of phase with *A*.

One can readily recognize an advantage that two-phase current has over single-phase. *In single-phase alternating current the sine wave drops all of the way to zero* before it again rises in the opposite direction. Thus, there is a period of time, *for each cycle,* when the voltage is absolutely *zero.*

Although each *single* sine wave also drops to zero in two-phase a.c., it is readily noticeable that the fall of one sine wave is met by the rise of the other. The *effective voltage* is thus bound to be higher than in the single-phase.

Three-Phase A.C. Generator

A three-phase generator has three single-phase windings equidistantly spaced around the rotor. Being spaced in this manner the induced a.c. voltage in one winding is 120° out of phase with the other two. The simplified windings are shown in the illustration below, together with a diagram of the resulting wave form.

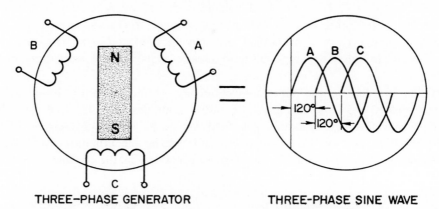

THREE—PHASE GENERATOR   THREE-PHASE SINE WAVE

The above diagram shows six wires emerging from the stator. This would be wasteful in terms of the number of wires which would have to be used in order to take advantage of this more efficient current. Instead, two other methods have been devised for connecting the three windings.

The Star Connection

One method for connecting the six wires is called the "wye" or "star" connection. The point at which all coils connect is the neutral point, and the *phase voltage* is measured from that point to any one of the line leads. The *total* or *line voltage* is equal to the constant, 1.73, times the phase voltage.

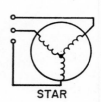

STAR

The Delta Connection

Another method for connecting the six wires is called the "delta." In the delta the phases are connected end to end. The *line current* is equal to 1.73 times the phase *current.*

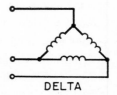

DELTA

The wave form shown in the circle above clearly indicates that the three-phase alternating current is even more efficient than the two-phase. Since this is true one may wonder why three-phase is not universally used for homes as well as for industry. The reason lies in the fact that three-phase does require additional wiring, more expensive transformers, and other additional expense. The added efficiency is not great enough to compensate for the added expense for home use.

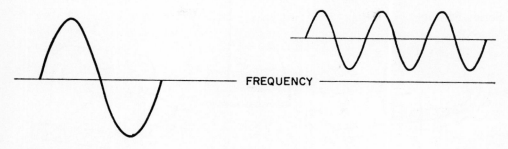

FREQUENCY

Frequency

The frequency produced by an alternating-current generator — alternator — is dependent upon the speed of the armature, and the number of poles in the field windings. The higher the speed, and the greater the number of poles, the higher is the generated frequency.

Voltage

In the case of the *simplified* generators shown in the two- and three-phase generators, the strength of the rotating bar magnet influences the output voltage. The stronger the magnet, the higher the voltage induced into the windings. It should again be pointed out that this type of generator is rare. It was presented in the two-phase and three-phase illustrations because of its simplicity. It is also a fact that the simplified drawings could be used because the *principle* of operation is the same as the generator in which the field supplies the electromagnetic lines of force, and the induced voltage is picked off from the armature. Most commercial generators employ the latter, and are considered conventional design. Many times these "generators" are referred to as *alternators*.

In *conventional* alternator design, the voltage and current are picked off from the slip rings of the armature. The voltage output from the conventional alternator depends upon the field current. The greater the amperage through the field winding, the higher the induced voltage in the rotor winding.

Since the amount of load to which an alternator is connected directly influences the output voltage, some method must be used to compensate for varying loads. This is accomplished by varying the amount of amperage fed into the field winding. The amperage, in turn, directly controls the number of the electromagnetic lines of force in the field, and therefore the voltage output. Feeding a direct current to the field winding for the purpose of creating electromagnetic lines of force is sometimes referred to as *exciting the field*.

175

THE ALTERNATING-CURRENT MOTOR

Today the alternating-current motor is far more popular than the direct-current motor, representing more than 95 percent of the motors used in home appliances, and it accounts for nearly that percentage in industry.

Series Motors

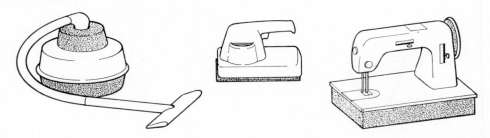

One of the most common a.c. motors used in both home and industry is the so-called a.c. *series* motor, which is also called the *universal* motor. Its latter name has been earned because it can be used with *either* alternating current *or* direct current. It is used in portable saws, sanders, sewing machines, vacuum cleaners, portable drills, and hundreds of other devices.

The series motor has an armature with commutator and brushes. The field winding and armature are connected in series with the power source. Brushes feed the voltage to the armature by means of the commutator.

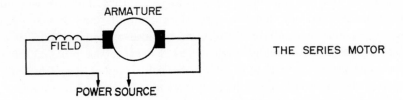

THE SERIES MOTOR

One may wonder how it is possible to use a series-wired motor with an alternating current when the current is continuously reversing.

It should be recalled that earlier in this unit the reversal of the direction of rotation of an armature was discussed. At that time it was stated that in order to reverse armature travel it is necessary to reverse the current flow to *either* the armature *or* the field winding, but not to both. It was pointed out that reversing the current to *both* armature *and* field results in the armature turning in the same direction as it did originally.

Alternating current effectively does the latter. As it reverses its direction of flow, it actually reverses the current to *both* the field *and* the armature, thus resulting in a continuous armature travel in one direction. To reverse the direction of rotation, one must reverse *either* the wire to the field, *or* to the armature.

The series a.c. motor, like the series d.c. motor, has good starting torque, but its speed tends to vary with load.

Split-Phase Motors

The split-phase motor is a *single-phase* motor which makes use of the principle of induction for its operation. It has a field winding, and it has an armature. *But* the armature contains no commutator, and there are no brushes.

Since there are no brushes and no commutator, one might wonder how the source voltage is fed to the armature. It is not, at least not directly.

A voltage does get to the armature, and a current does flow within the armature, but it is accomplished by means of induction. Because induction has been explained previously, it is only necessary to hastily review the action.

If a conductor, such as a copper rod, *A*, is connected to a galvanometer and laid alongside another copper rod, *B*, which in turn is connected to a strong alternating-voltage source, the expanding and contracting magnetic lines of flux from *B* cut across conductor *A* and induce a voltage within it. Thus, although *A* is not *physically* connected to a voltage source, a voltage is present and current does flow.

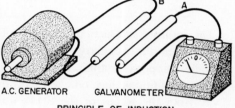

PRINCIPLE OF INDUCTION

The split-phase motor uses the principle of induction for its operation. Unlike the armature of the d.c. motor, or the series a.c. motor, which is built up from many turns of relatively fine wire connected to commutator segments, the split-phase armature — or rotor — is made of heavy copper bars which are joined at the ends by heavy copper rings. Between the copper bars are lengths of laminated iron. The entire assembly is many times referred to as a *squirrel-cage rotor*.

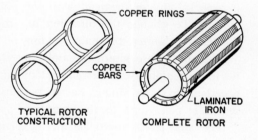

As an alternating current flows through the field winding of a split-phase motor, a voltage is induced into the rotor, and a current flows in the copper bars. The induced current is always opposite to the inducing current, hence, the polarity in the rotor is opposite from that in the field winding.

Because opposite poles attract it seems that the rotor and stator should lock in place and refuse to turn. That is exactly what would happen if it were not for a *second* field winding called the starting or auxiliary winding. The manner in which the auxiliary winding is placed in relationship to the main winding, the difference in the size and length of wire used for both windings, and the interaction of these factors create a "rotating field." This simply means that the polarity is caused to *revolve* around the field windings.

As the motor comes up to about 70 percent of its rated speed, the auxiliary winding is cut out of the circuit by means of an automatic switch. The *revolving polarity is maintained* by the *interaction* between the changing polarity of the main winding, and that of the rotor. Never at any time is there direct physical connection between the rotor and main winding. This latter fact is clearly shown in the schematic diagram below.

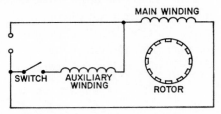

SPLIT PHASE MOTOR

The induced interaction between rotor and main field winding is the important factor once the auxiliary winding has been eliminated from the circuit. What actually happens is this: a motor which is operating under normal load and voltage conditions has one loop of the rotor (two copper bars) which is 90° away from the forces of the field's attraction and repulsion. The rotor tries desperately to catch up to the revolving field — and lock in place — but it cannot because of its own weight, because of bearing friction, and because of the load and wind resistance as the armature turns. The revolving polarity of the field is able to stay in the lead with the polarity of the armature trailing by a split second. To change the direction of armature rotation, it is necessary to switch the leads to *either* the main winding *or* the starting winding.

The split-phase motor has only fair starting torque. Its more desirable features lie in its simplicity of design and operation, and in the fact that it has excellent speed control. Its simple design permits reduced manufacturing costs, a savings which is passed on to the consumer.

The split-phase motor is an inexpensive device which can be used to good advantage with applications which do not present heavy starting loads. Jig saws, light-duty bench grinders, washing machines, and hundreds of other machines use the simple, trouble-free split-phase motor.

Capacitor-Start Motors

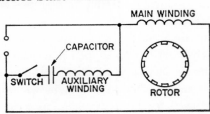

CAPACITOR START MOTOR

A capacitor-start motor is very similar to the split phase, except that it has a capacitor in series with the auxiliary winding. The capacitor helps provide the needed revolving field, and it provides a much better starting torque. It also has excellent speed-control characteristics.

As the rotor comes up to 70 percent of its rated speed, a switch opens the circuit to the capacitor and auxiliary winding, leaving only the main winding physically connected to the a.c. source.

Like the split-phase motor, the capacitor-start motor has no commutator or brushes which need maintenance. The squirrel-cage rotor has no winding to burn out. It is inexpensive to maintain and simple to operate. Because of its ability to start heavy loads it is often found on air compressors, pumps, circular saws, and other machinery which demands a high starting torque.

Other Motors

There are many other types of motors in the a.c. family, but those already mentioned are by far the most popular. Among the others are synchronous motors which operate clocks, shaded-pole motors which run light-duty fans, and three-phase motors which are found throughout industry.

Generally speaking the fractional-horsepower motors — those of less than 1 horsepower — are primarily the motors which were explained in detail in this unit. Motors having ratings greater than 1 horsepower very often are three phase.

REVIEW QUESTIONS

1. When using the left-hand rule for finding the polarity of an electromagnet, the fingers point in the direction of electron flow, and the thumb points in the direction of the _____ pole.

2. The flux lines of a magnet are assumed to travel from the _____ pole to the _____ pole.

3. When applying the left-hand rule for finding the direction of electron flow in the armature of a generator, the middle finger points in the direction of _____ _____.

4. When applying the left-hand rule for generators, the forefinger, middle finger, and thumb should all be at _____° to one another.

5. Direct current always flows in _____ direction/s.

6. A commutator is found on a/an _____ _____ generator.

7. Slip rings are found on a/an _____ _____ generator.

8. To reverse the direction of rotation of a direct-current motor, one should reverse the wires to either the field winding, or to the _____.

9. To vary the speed of a direct-current motor, a _____ is often used.

10. A direct-current motor having its field and armature wired in shunt has a _____ starting torque.

11. A direct-current motor having its field and armature wired in series has _____ speed regulation.

12. Direct-current motors having relatively good speed control, and good starting torque are said to be _____ wired.

13. An alternating-current generator having a single set of poles will generate a/an _____-phase voltage.

14. Alternating current flows in _____ direction/s.

15. The "star" and "delta" connections are associated with the _____-phase alternating-current generator.

16. A motor having no commutator or brushes is called a/an _____ motor.

17. Capacitor-start motors have a fairly _____ starting torque and good speed control.

Unit 14

ALTERNATING CURRENT

Alternating current has already been discussed briefly in the unit on generators and motors. This present unit provides greater depth in understanding this type of electrical energy.

Alternating current flows back and forth in a conductor at specifically timed intervals. It first goes in one direction, and then reverses to go in the opposite direction. One might compare a.c. with d.c. in the following manner.

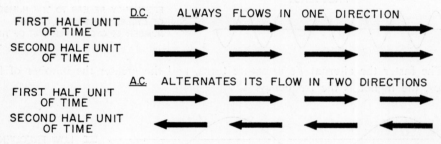

Although the above diagrams provide a visual comparison of the reversal of alternating current, they do not show how a.c. builds from zero voltage to maximum, then falls back to zero to build again to maximum in the opposite direction, only to again return to zero, and on and on. This latter concept can be better shown with the use of a graph.

Alternations

The graph is referred to as a *waveform*. The top half of the waveform is called a *positive alternation,* and the bottom half is called a *negative alternation.* Two alternations equal *one cycle.* One cycle is equivalent to 360° rotation of the armature of a single-phase a.c. generator.

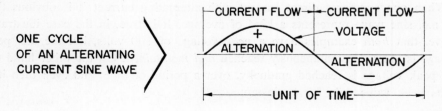

ONE CYCLE OF AN ALTERNATING CURRENT SINE WAVE

It will be noticed that the voltage does *not* immediately rise to maximum, but rather ascends relatively gradually over a definite period or unit of time. This results in a kind of "average" voltage which must be considered when solving mathematical problems dealing with a.c.

The diagram below illustrates how the gradual rise and fall of the sine wave occurs as the alternator's armature rotates in the magnetic lines of flux.

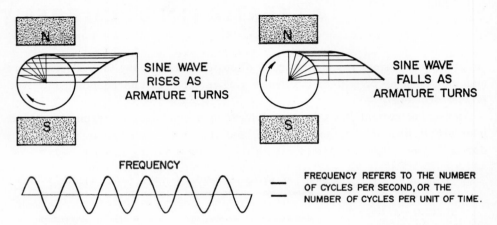

The faster the alternator's armature turns, and the greater the number of field poles, the higher is the frequency.

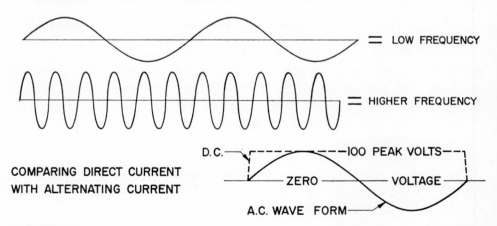

Peak Voltage

When one compares direct current with alternating current it is obvious that the a.c. sine wave represents a kind of average. It is true, in the case illustrated above, that *both* examples have a *peak* voltage of 100 volts, but the d.c. peak voltage is almost instantaneously reached *and maintained*. On the other hand the a.c. peak voltage is reached gradually, over a period of time, and even then it is at its peak value only for an instant.

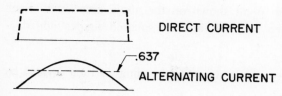

DIRECT CURRENT

AVERAGE VOLTAGE IS THE SAME AS ITS MAXIMUM (PEAK) VALUE.

ALTERNATING CURRENT

THE ARITHMETICAL AVERAGE IS EQUIVALENT TO .637 OF ITS MAXIMUM (PEAK) VALUE.

Judging from the above illustrations one might be led to believe that 1 alternation of alternating current is equivalent to .637 of the value of 1 pulsation of direct current, for the same unit of time. It is true that .637 is the *mathematical* average of a sine wave. It is *not* true that the *power* which can be delivered by an a.c. wave form is equal to .637 of a similar pulse of d.c.

Effective Voltage

To the contrary, it has been found that a peak voltage of alternating current is equivalent to .707 of a similar direct-current voltage when *power* is being considered. The .707 figure represents *effective* voltage, or that voltage which can accomplish useful work. For example, to find the *effective* voltage of 100 *peak* volts, it is necessary to multiply peak volts × the mathematical constant, .707, or $100 \times .707 = 70.7$ effective volts.

D.C. = 100 PEAK VOLTS = 100 EFFECTIVE VOLTS

A.C. = 100 PEAK VOLTS = 70.7 EFFECTIVE VOLTS

The .707 figure is a mathematical constant which is computed by a method called *root mean square*. Root mean square, or r.m.s., as it is more often known, can be better understood when referred to a diagram.

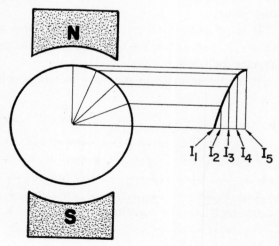

As the armature of an alternating-current generator revolves, the instantaneous current flow from the slip rings can be graphed directly into an a.c. sine wave form as shown. Thus, I_1, I_2, and so on represent instantaneous amperage figures.

185

The current is measured at each point shown on the above sine wave. Each measured amperage reading is then squared, and all squared figures added.

$$I_1^2 + I_2^2 + I_3^2 + I_4^2 + I_5^2 = I_T^2$$

The sum of the squares of the measured amperage readings is then divided by the number of measurements taken.

$$I_T \div 5 = Average \text{ of the sum of the squares of the } I\text{'s.}$$

The square root is then taken of the computed average.

$$\sqrt{\substack{\text{R.M.S. (Effective Value)} \\ \text{Average of the Sum of the} \\ \text{Squares of the } I\text{'s}}}$$

The answer is .707 of the peak amperage. It is that *effective value* which can do useful work.

Effective *voltage* can be computed in the same manner.

The diagram showing the armature and resulting wave form with the instantaneous amperages shows only five measurements of *I*. It should be pointed out that this number was arbitrarily chosen for simplicity. Actually, a much greater number of readings had to be used originally in order to secure a more accurate r.m.s value of .707.

REMEMBER

The R.M.S. value of .707 represents the value, of a sine wave, which is effective. It is that figure which gets work accomplished. (The .637 value is merely an arithmetic average.)

Almost all a.c. meters indicate the *effective* value of alternating current. A.c. voltmeters indicate .707 of the peak voltage because they are calibrated to show that value.

It is possible to secure meters which also indicate values *other* than effective values. It is possible, for example, to secure meters which indicate the arithmetic average of .637.

It is also possible to purchase meters which indicate *peak* values, or *peak-to-peak* indications.

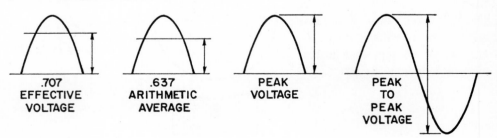

| .707 EFFECTIVE VOLTAGE | .637 ARITHMETIC AVERAGE | PEAK VOLTAGE | PEAK TO PEAK VOLTAGE |

At this point it may be well to use actual figures to summarize the various voltage figures. The same figures, of course, could be applied to amperage. The following sine wave and voltage values will help in this summary.

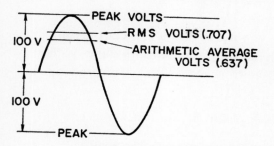

PEAK TO PEAK VOLTS =
2 X 100 = 200 VOLTS

PEAK VOLTS = 100 VOLTS

ARITHMETIC AVERAGE VOLTS =
.637 X 100 = 63.7 VOLTS

EFFECTIVE VOLTS =
.707 X 100 = 70.7 VOLTS

COMPARISON OF ALTERNATING CURRENT VOLTAGES

True Effective Voltage

At this point a possible misconception should be cleared up. Since the peak-to-peak voltage shown in the illustration equals 200 volts, one might mistakenly believe that the *true* effective voltage should be 141.4 volts, or .707 × 200.

This is not the case!

One must remember that the peak-to-peak volts are secured from the graph. The alternating current being generated does not rise from zero to 200 volts, but rather from zero to 100 volts in *one* direction, and then from zero to 100 volts in the *opposite* direction. The useful voltage — r.m.s. or effective voltage — cannot possibly be peak-to-peak times .707, but rather zero-to-peak times .707.

If one were to mistakenly believe that the peak-to-peak value should be used, then it would be just as easy to mistakenly believe that the effective voltage should be zero, because the *positive* alternation above the zero line *seemingly* should be mathematically cancelled out by the *negative* alternation below the line. This, of course, is known to be false, because alternating current can accomplish just as much work when the electrons are flowing in one direction as it can when the electrons are flowing in the opposite direction.

At this point another clarification should also be made. In the unit on generators and motors, pulsating direct current was shown as the illustration *A* represents it. In this unit pulsating direct current was shown as in *B*. This apparent inconsistency can easily be explained. The pulsations shown in the unit on generators resulted from the revolving of an armature in a magnetic field of flux.

The pulsations discussed in this unit, and shown in *B,* were those which might come from a battery as a switch is quickly opened and closed.

Comparisons between a.c. and d.c. are almost always carried out with the direct current as it would appear in a battery circuit.

<blockquote>

REMEMBER

Effective, or R.M.S., voltage is that electrical pressure most often used in solving problems dealing with electronics. It is the voltage most often indicated by A.C. meters.

Peak Voltage × .707 = R.M.S. or Effective Volts

</blockquote>

One might wonder whether it is possible to determine the peak voltage provided an effective voltage is given. Of course! One simply uses the mathematical constant 1.414 and multiplies that figure times the r.m.s. value. The alert student will notice that 1.414 is the reciprocal of .707.

Example
Given: 100 volts r.m.s.
Find: Peak volts
Solution: $1.414 \times$ r.m.s. volts $= 1.414 \times 100 = 141.4$ peak volts

Summary Review Problems

■ **Problem 1**
Given: 170 *Peak* Volts
Find: R.M.S. Volts
Answer: 120.19 Volts, *R.M.S.*

■ **Problem 2**
Given: 100 *Peak* Volts
Find: *Average* Volts
Answer: 63.7 Volts *Average*

■ **Problem 3**
Given: 110 R.M.S. Volts
Find: *Peak* Volts
Answer: 155.54 Volts *Peak*

■ **Problem 4**
Given: 150 *Peak* Volts
Find: *Peak-to-Peak* Volts
Answer: 300 Volts *Peak to Peak*

■ **Problem 5**
Given: 100 Volts R.M.S.
Find: *Peak-to-Peak* Volts
Answer: 282.8 Volts *Peak to Peak*

Pure Resistance in A.C. Circuits

All alternating-current circuits contain some pure ohmic resistance such as one finds in a strictly carbon resistor. If all a.c. circuits contained *only* pure ohmic resistance, as measured directly by an ohmmeter, Ohm's Law could be used for all calculations involving resistance, voltage, and amperage. As this unit will later reveal, this is not the case, and Ohm's Law must be modified when it is used to solve many alternating-current problems.

In an a.c. circuit containing *only* pure ohmic resistance, the voltage and current are *in phase*.

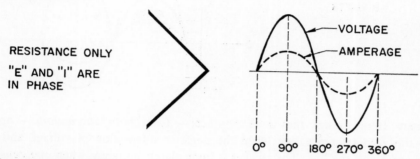

RESISTANCE ONLY

"E" AND "I" ARE IN PHASE

What does this mean?

Thus far voltage and amperage have been dealt with separately. It is a fact that one can properly show a voltage waveform because it is absolutely possible to generate a voltage without having that voltage do anything, such as having it push electrons through a conductor. After all, charged batteries have a certain voltage, but no current flows until the battery in connected to a circuit.

Technically speaking, it is not appropriate to diagram an amperage waveform without showing it in relationship to a voltage sine wave, because an amperage is never possible without an accompanying voltage.

When voltage and amperage are *in phase* they rise and fall together, crossing the zero reference line at exactly the same points. The height of the voltage waveform is determined by the voltage source. The height of the amperage sine wave depends upon the amount of resistance present for the given voltage.

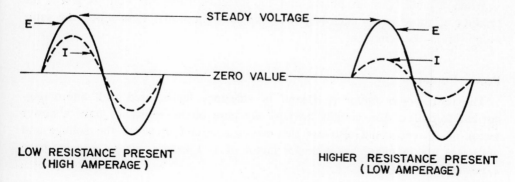

LOW RESISTANCE PRESENT
(HIGH AMPERAGE)

HIGHER RESISTANCE PRESENT
(LOW AMPERAGE)

The power expended in any alternating-current circuit can be computed by multiplying the voltage times the amperage, provided that circuit contains *only* *pure ohmic resistance.*

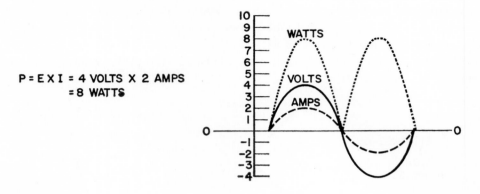

P = E X I = 4 VOLTS X 2 AMPS
= 8 WATTS

It may seem strange that *both* products — from *both alternations* — appear above the zero reference line when the negative alternation of voltage and amperage are *below* the line. The answer is immediately apparent when one considers that anytime *two* negative numbers are multiplied, the product becomes positive.

It must be borne in mind, however, that the rules regarding peak and r.m.s. values must still be observed. In the above illustration the answer of eight watts is in *peak* watts. To find effective watts, or r.m.s. wattage, it is necessary to multiply the r.m.s. values of *E* and *I*.

REMEMBER
When an alternating current circuit contains ONLY pure ohmic resistance, Ohm's law can be applied directly, and the power formula is simply, $P = E \times I$.

When *E* and *I* are in phase, and the effective value for both is given, the product of those two values is power expressed in watts. It is much the same as power in d.c. circuits.

Power Factor

The term *power factor* is a kind of efficiency figure used with alternating-current formulas. A.c. circuits having *only* pure ohmic resistance have a power factor of 1. One could also say that any a.c. circuit in which the voltage and amperage are *in phase* has a power factor of 1. Likewise, *all d.c. circuits* have a power factor of 1.

In the next section of this unit it will be shown that alternating-current circuits may have what is known as *reactance*. Such circuits have power factors *less than 1*. This fact must be taken into consideration when determining certain mathematical relationships in a.c. An alternating-current formula in which power factor must be considered is the power formula, which is shown below.

MODIFIED
A.C. POWER ➤ $P = E \times I \times P.F.$
FORMULA

In this formula, p.f. — power factor — is usually expressed as a decimal, such as .7, or .8, or .61. It is also possible to express power factor in terms of a percentage, such as 70%, or 80%, or 61%.

It may now be understood why the a.c. circuit illustrated on the preceding page could use the d.c. version of the power formula without having to consider power factor. Since the circuit obviously contained only pure ohmic resistance, with E and I in phase, the formula could simply and correctly be stated as $P = EI$.

Why is this so? Because $P = EI$ is the same as $P = E \times I \times 1$. The power factor 1 could not possibly have changed the answer, and therefore was properly omitted from the formula. True, the entire modified formula may have been used; the answer would have been the same.

INDUCTANCE IN A.C. CIRCUITS

Whenever an electric current flows through a conductor, such as a copper wire, a magnetic field is present. As the current increases, the magnetic field expands, and as the current decreases the lines of flux recede back into the conductor.

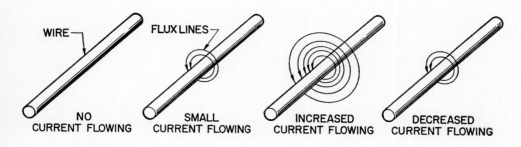

WIRE FLUX LINES

NO
CURRENT FLOWING

SMALL
CURRENT FLOWING

INCREASED
CURRENT FLOWING

DECREASED
CURRENT FLOWING

A changing magnetic field results in a phenomenon known as *inductance*. Inductance is that electrical characteristic which results in *opposition* to any change in circuit current. Inductance is designated by the symbol **L.** It results in a form of electrical resistance.

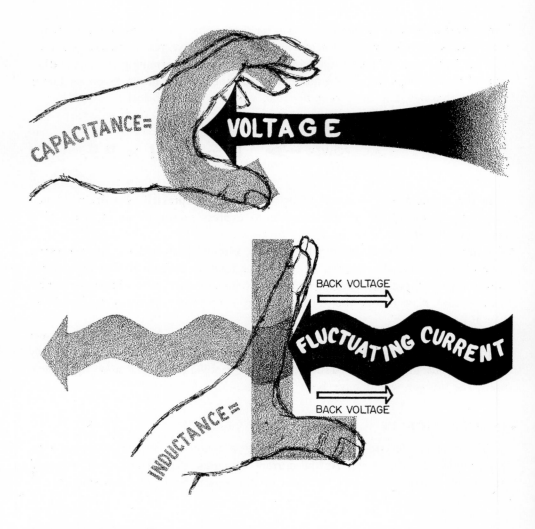

What causes inductance?

Expanding and contracting magnetic flux lines cut across the wire in which a fluctuating current is flowing, thus inducing or "generating" a *back voltage* in that same conductor. Instead of speaking of a back voltage, the name *inductance* was coined, and the *unit* of inductance is the *henry*.

In order to define a henry, it is said that 1 henry of inductance is present when a change in current of 1 ampere per second produces an induced pressure of 1 volt.

Because a henry is relatively large for many electronic applications, the millihenry and microhenry are often used.

$$1 \text{ millihenry (mh)} = .001 \text{ henry, or } 1 \times 10^{-3}$$
$$1 \text{ microhenry } (\mu h) = .000001 \text{ henry, or } 1 \times 10^{-6}$$

Factors Affecting Inductance

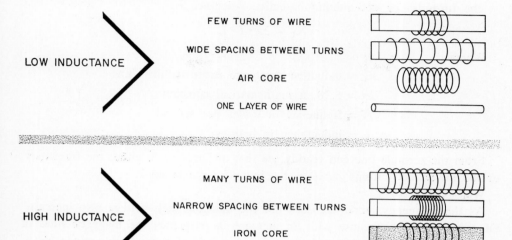

The number of turns of wire, the spacing between the turns, the kind of core material upon which the windings are wound, and the number of layers of windings are factors affecting the inductance of a coil of wire and the effect the coil has upon the circuit in which it is connected.

Other factors which also affect inductance, but to a lesser degree, are the diameter of the form upon which the windings are placed, the wire size, and the type of winding.

REMEMBER

Inductance OPPOSES CHANGES in current flow.

Inductive Reactance

Inductance is only a part of the whole story. Inductance is a static thing. For example, a coil of wire may have a certain amount of rated inductance, but it would not be an important factor if used in a direct-current circuit, for in a d.c. circuit the coil would affect current only because of the pure ohmic resistance present. On the other hand, if that same coil were placed in an a.c. circuit, it would contain not only the same pure ohmic resistance as in the d.c. circuit, but it would also have *inductive reactance*.

Inductive reactance is a dynamic characteristic. It is a form of resistance, resistance which changes as frequency and inductance change. The higher the

193

frequency, and the higher the henry rating, the higher is the inductive reactance.

The formula for determining inductive reactance is:

$$X_L = 2\pi \cdot f \cdot L$$

Where:

X_L = inductive reactance expressed in ohms

2π = 6.28, a mathematical constant

f = frequency in cycles per second

L = inductance in henries

From the formula one can readily see that an increase in either the frequency, or the inductance rating, increases the inductive reactance.

Why is this so?

As the frequency increases, does not the induced back voltage also increase? Of course it does, because with an increase in frequency the magnetic lines of force cut across the windings more often in a unit of time. It is comparable to turning the armature of a d.c. generator faster in order to generate more voltage. This *back voltage* manifests itself in a retarding or repelling force, which acts like an added resistance, or X_L. Because it does manifest itself as a retarding factor it is expressed in ohms, *not* as "back voltage."

An inductor having a larger inductance rating produces the same results. It produces a greater back voltage, which is the same as saying that it produces a greater inductive reactance, X_L . . . a greater ohms value.

Instead of dealing with an answer in "so many units of inductive reactance" or X_L, the answer is expressed in *ohms*. Thus it is treated like any other retarding or repelling force.

But the story still is not complete.

Whenever inductive reactance comes into the picture strange and mysterious things begin to happen.

In an a.c. circuit having *only* pure ohmic resistance present, voltage and amperage rise and fall at the same time, crossing the zero reference line at the same points.

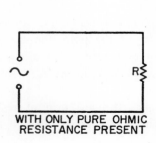

WITH ONLY PURE OHMIC
RESISTANCE PRESENT

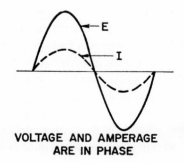

VOLTAGE AND AMPERAGE
ARE IN PHASE

This is *not true* in an inductive circuit. The current in an inductive circuit does not begin to rise at the same instant that voltage rises. The *current* is *delayed* by an amount of time depending upon the amount of inductance in the circuit as contrasted to the amount of pure ohmic resistance.

If it were possible — which it is not — to have a circuit containing *only* inductance, the amperage would be 90° out of phase with the voltage.

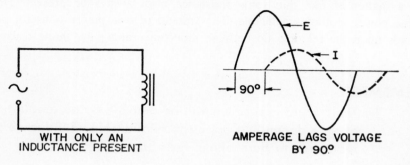

WITH ONLY AN
INDUCTANCE PRESENT

AMPERAGE LAGS VOLTAGE
BY 90°

In such cases in which amperage lags behind voltage by 90° the useful power — *true power* — is equal to *zero!* This seems incredible when one recognizes that an actual voltage is present, and a current does flow. Earlier it was taught that power equals volts times amperes, *but* it was also stated that the standard power formula must be changed when dealing with alternating current. This is a case in point.

How is it possible that power can equal zero with a voltage and amperage present? One way to understand this is by the use of graphs. The following graph shows voltage, amperage, and power plotted for a theoretical circuit having only inductance with no resistance. Remember that power is the product of voltage times amperage. Also remember that any time a positive number is multiplied by a negative number, the result — the product — is *negative*.

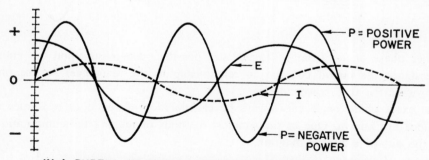

IN A PURELY INDUCTIVE CIRCUIT, VOLTAGE AND AMPERAGE
ARE OUT OF PHASE BY 90° —— TRUE POWER IS ZERO

One may divide the waveform into as many vertical lines as desired. Multiply $E \times I$. One will soon discover that a power waveform can be plotted from the products of the instantaneous measurements taken, but something important happens — there are as many *negative* power alternations as there are positive power alternations. When the negative and positive are added the net result is *zero*. *No useful power is available,* because both power alternations do not appear above the zero reference line as they did in the purely resistive circuit shown previously.

It is a matter of fact that some resistance must always be present. Hence, some true power is always available. The amount of true power — useful power — depends upon the relationship between inductance and pure ohmic resistance.

REMEMBER

The current in a circuit will be delayed by an amount of time depending upon the relationship of inductive reactance to pure ohmic resistance.

Phase Angle

If *equal* amounts of inductive reactance and pure ohmic resistance are present in a circuit, the voltage and current are 45° out of phase. This means that the *current lags the voltage* by 45°.

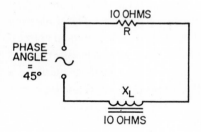
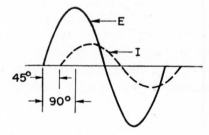

Other phase angles from 0° to 90° are possible, depending upon the amount of resistance the circuit contains in relationship to the reactance. As the phase angle varies the true power varies.

The exact phase angle can always be calculated provided both resistance and reactance are known. One of the simplest methods of making the computation is with the aid of a vector diagram.

An Example

Find the phase angle, and the *total* resistance of a circuit having the following amount of inductive reactance and pure ohmic resistance:

196

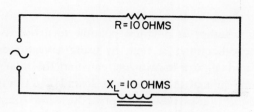

R = 10 OHMS

X$_L$ = 10 OHMS

Procedure:

1. Using graph paper, or some kind of measuring device, lay off the vector R to a length of 10 units along a horizontal line.

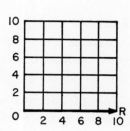

2. Using the same graph paper or measuring device, lay off X_L at right angles, upward, from the start of R.

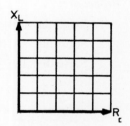

3. Complete a parallelogram, and draw a line diagonally from the intersection of R and X_L to the opposite corner. The diagonal line should be labeled Z.

   The phase angle is the angle between Z and R.

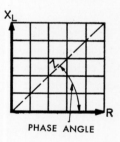

PHASE ANGLE

4. That is not all. The diagonal line Z is also important because it represents what is known as "impedance." Impedance is the *total* resistance of R *and* X_L.

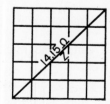

One cannot simply *add* R and X_L because of the fact that the phase angle is involved, which in turn affects the lag of current behind voltage. The two components of R and X_L must be referred to special mathematical treatment. Simple addition will not do!

Impedance

One may wonder whether or not it is possible to arrive at the total a.c. resistance — Z — in any other manner than by using a vector diagram. The answer is, "Yes." Once R and X_L are known one can find the total resistance by taking the square root of the sum of the squares of R and X_L. Complicated? Not really. The following example breaks down the procedure into simple steps.

Example

Assume the circuit illustrated at the right has equal amounts of pure ohmic resistance and inductive reactance amounting to 10 ohms each.

What is the *total* impedance, Z (a.c. resistance)?

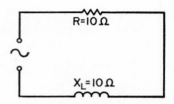

Procedure:

1. State the formula: $Z = \sqrt{R^2 + X_L^2}$
2. Substitute in the formula: $\sqrt{(10)^2 + (10)^2}$
3. Solve for the answer: $\sqrt{100 + 100} = \sqrt{200} =$
   14.14 ohms total impedance

REMEMBER

Z = Impedance = Total A.C. resistance

One may now wonder whether or not it is possible to determine the *true power* of a circuit which has R, X_L, and Z. Again the answer is, "Yes." The true power can be calculated by referring to the new, modified, a.c. power formula:

THE FORMULA

$P = E \times I \times P.F.$

"But," one might say, "how is power factor — p.f. — determined? It is not given."

No, it is not given, but it can be calculated; and once p.f. has been determined, one may substitute directly in the modified power formula.

Before calculating power factor one may be interested in knowing from where it comes. Power factor is known, mathematically, as the cosine of the phase angle.

What does this mean?

It can be more easily understood by again referring to the impedance triangle illustrated previously.

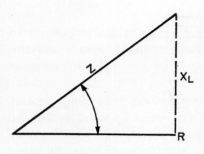

The pure ohmic resistance forms the base. The inductive reactance forms the right angle to the base.

The third side, the hypotenuse, is the resulting impedance, Z.

The phase angle formed by the Z and R sides of the triangle is known mathematically by the name of *theta* (θ), a Greek letter. The *cosine* of the phase angle is the ratio of R to Z, and is written

$$\text{Cos } \theta = \frac{R}{Z}$$

and, power factor is the same as cosine theta (cos θ).

In summary, then, one can determine p.f. by finding the ratio of R to Z, thus:

$$\text{P.F.} = \frac{R}{Z}$$

which is the same as saying cos $\theta = \dfrac{R}{Z}$, because power factor *is* cosine theta.

The modified power formula can be written in several ways:

$$P = E \times I \times \text{P.F.}$$

$$or \quad P = E \times I \times \frac{R}{Z}$$

$$or \quad P = E \times I \times \cos \theta$$

All formulas mean exactly the same thing, but since it is well to have uniformity and consistency in treatment, this text uses the first of the three formulas for determining power factor in a.c. circuits.

A Summary

Put all of the foregoing information together and find the *true power* for the following problem:

Given: E = 50 volts
        I = 10 amperes
        R = 3 ohms
       X_L = 4 ohms
        Z = 5 ohms

Procedure:

1. Find: Cos $\theta = \dfrac{R}{Z} = \dfrac{3}{5}$ (this is the same as P.F.)

2. Write the formula for *true power*: $P = E \times I \times \text{P.F.}$

3. Substitute and solve: $P = E \times I \times \text{P.F.} = 50 \times 10 \times .6 = 300$ watts

199

Apparent Power

Several examples have now been given for *true power* in a.c. circuits. What is *apparent power?* Apparent power is simply the product of voltage and amperage. It is the power one might *assume* he has in an a.c. circuit if he forgets about phase angle.

In d.c. circuits apparent power and true power are the same thing because voltage and current are *always* in phase. In an a.c. circuit apparent power and true power may not be the same. Apparent power is merely that which *appears* to be the useful available power, but actually is not. True power is the actual power available to do useful work. One can determine true power in an alternating-current network provided he knows the value of E, L, and p.f. ($\cos \theta$).

A Review

To review each of the concepts in its proper relationship to the whole it is well to solve a problem completely through from its beginning.

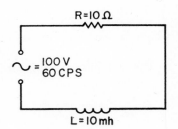

Using the schematic diagram shown at the right, find the values of the following: X_L, Z, p.f., true power, apparent power.

Procedure

1. Find X_L (inductive reactance):
$$X_L = 2\pi f L = 6.28 \times 60 \times .010 = 3.77 \text{ ohms}$$
(NOTE: 10 mh. had to be changed to .010 henry)

2. Find Z (impedance):
$$Z = \sqrt{R^2 + X_L^2} = \sqrt{(10)^2 + (3.77)^2} = \sqrt{100 + 14.2}$$
$$\sqrt{114.2} = 10.7 \text{ ohms}$$

3. Find p.f. (power factor, or $\cos \theta$):
$$\text{P.F.} = \frac{R}{Z} = \frac{10}{10.7} = .936$$

4. Find the true power:
$$\text{True Power} = E \times I \times \text{P.F.} = 100 \times 9.36 \times .936 = 876 \text{ watts}$$
$$\left(I = \frac{E}{Z} = \frac{100}{10.7} = 9.36 \right)$$

5. Find the apparent power:
$$\text{Apparent Power} = E \times I = 100 \times 9.36 = 936 \text{ watts}$$

Uses of Inductive Reactance

Can inductive reactance serve any useful purpose? Yes!

1. It is used as a "choke" to filter out the ripples which are found in power supplies which have converted a.c. to d.c.
2. It is used for controlling current flow, and power factor, in many circuits such as theater light dimming circuits.
3. Its principles are used in transformers and motors, thus making these devices more efficient.
4. It is used in radio and television tuning circuits, and in hundreds of other very common and useful electronic devices.

What does all of the foregoing mean when presented in practical terms?

It means that any a.c. series circuit having both resistance and inductive reactance will have a greater total resistance than a d.c. series circuit with the same resistive components.

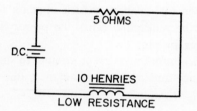

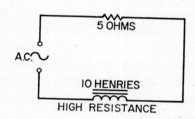

This is true because the 10-henry coil in the d.c. circuit contains only pure ohmic resistance for that circuit. In the a.c. circuit the same coil has both pure ohmic resistance and inductive reactance. Not only does the a.c. circuit have a greater total resistance, but the inductive reactance causes the current to lag the voltage, thus causing an out-of-phase condition which results in a lowered power factor and a smaller true power.

If the frequency of the alternating-current circuit is increased, or if the inductance of the coil increases, the X_L of the circuit becomes even greater resulting in a lower true power.

The windings of a transformer, and the windings of an electric motor use the principle of inductive reactance to prevent a high current flow. Without X_L the efficiency of either device would be extremely low. In fact neither would function at all.

Although it may seem that inductive reactance is an unfortunate limiter of current, it is a fact that the world of electronics would be completely non-existent without it.

Review the Facts

1. Inductance results in opposition to a change in current.

2. Inductive reactance is a form of resistance which is measured in ohms and represented by the symbol X_L.

   Inductive reactance is equal to the constant, 6.28, times the frequency in cycles per second, times inductance in henries, or $X_L = 2\pi f L$.

3. Phase angle indicates the degree to which current lags behind voltage in an inductive circuit.

4. Power factor is the ratio of resistance to impedance, or $\dfrac{R}{Z}$. It is the same as cosine theta . . . cos θ.

   Power factor is usually thought of as being less than 1.00 (100%) in an alternating-current circuit.

5. True power is the product of *apparent* power times cos θ. It is the same as $E \times I \times \cos \theta$, or $E \times I \times$ P.F.

6. Apparent power is the product of voltage times amperage. In a direct-current circuit apparent power is always the same as the true power. In an alternating-current circuit apparent power is that wattage which appears to be expended in a circuit, but which must be multiplied times the power factor in order to determine the actual power present.

7. Impedance is the *total resistance* in an alternating-current circuit. In an a.c. circuit having both pure ohmic resistance and inductive reactance, one may find the total resistance by using the formula $Z = \sqrt{R^2 + X_L^2}$. The letter Z is the symbol for impedance.

CAPACITANCE IN A.C. CIRCUITS

Capacitors are components which store an electrical charge. They are made of two or more conductors, such as aluminum plates, which are separated by an insulator, such as air, waxed paper, mica, or other nonconductive materials. Capacitors are rated in microfarads, or micromicrofarads.

A capacitor would be rated at 1 farad if it could store 1 coulomb of charge with 1 volt of pressure applied to its plates. Since a farad is an unusually large rating, capacitors used in electronics are rated in microfarads — millionths of a farad — or in micromicrofarads — million millionths of a farad.

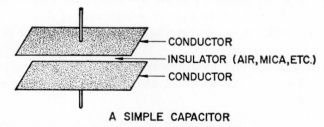

CONDUCTOR
INSULATOR (AIR, MICA, ETC.)
CONDUCTOR

A SIMPLE CAPACITOR

1 microfarad (μf.) $=$ .000001 farad
$= 1 \times 10^{-6}$ farad

$$1 \text{ micromicrofarad } (\mu\mu\text{f.}) = .000000000001 \text{ farad}$$
$$= 1 \times 10^{-12} \text{ farad}$$

Capacitors exhibit an electrical phenomenon known as *capacitance*. Capacitance results in *opposition* to any change in circuit voltage. Capacitance is designated by the symbol **C.** It results in a form of electrical resistance.

Factors Affecting Capacitance

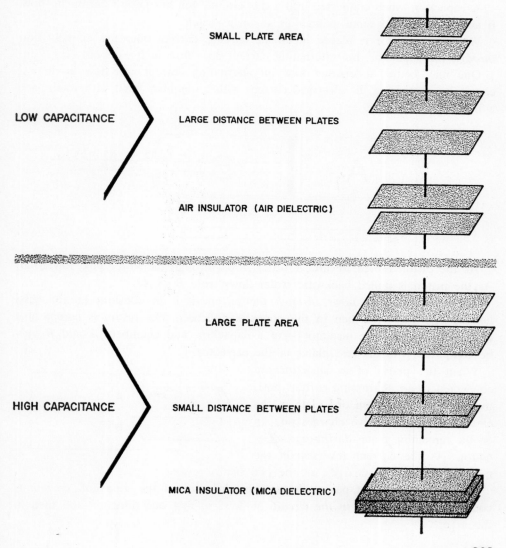

LOW CAPACITANCE

SMALL PLATE AREA

LARGE DISTANCE BETWEEN PLATES

AIR INSULATOR (AIR DIELECTRIC)

HIGH CAPACITANCE

LARGE PLATE AREA

SMALL DISTANCE BETWEEN PLATES

MICA INSULATOR (MICA DIELECTRIC)

The size of the plates, the spacing between the plates, and the material from which the insulator is made, are all factors affecting the capacitance.

Capacitors connected in *parallel add* capacitance. Capacitors connected in *series* result in a total capacitance which is smaller than that of the smallest capacitor.

REMEMBER

Capacitance OPPOSES CHANGES in voltage.

An Analogy

A capacitor, when connected into a d.c. circuit, will not permit current to flow. It acts in much the same manner as an open switch.

When a capacitor is placed in an a.c. circuit, current does not actually flow *through* the capacitor, but alternating current does flow in the circuit!

One may better understand how an alternating current can flow in an a.c. circuit by comparing the electrical current with a chamber filled with water, and a moving piston.

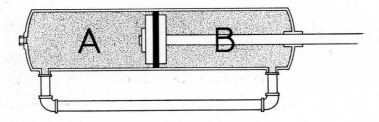

As the piston moves toward *A* water flows through the lower pipe toward *B*. As the piston is pulled backward water flows from *B* to *A*.

Although no water flows *through* the piston, it is in constant motion, first flowing one way and then in the opposite direction. The piston is comparable to the dielectric — the insulator — of a capacitor, and chambers *A* and *B* may be compared with the two plates of the capacitor.

When the plates of a capacitor are connected to an alternating current positive charges pile up on one plate of the capacitor while negative charges pile up on the remaining plate, *during one alternation.* As the current reverses on the 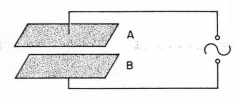 next alternation the charges on the two plates reverse.

Although no current passes *through* the dielectric of the capacitor, current is continuously in motion *in the circuit.* It flows in first one direction and then in the other.

Capacitive Reactance

Capacitors have a certain unique resistance to the flow of an alternating current. This resistance is called *capacitive reactance.*

The formula for determining capacitive reactance is:

$$X_C = \frac{1}{2\pi \cdot f \cdot C}$$

Where:

X_C = capacitive reactance expressed in ohms
2π = 6.28, a mathematical constant
f = frequency in cycles per second
C = capacitance expressed in farads

From the formula one can readily see that an increase in either frequency or capacitance *decreases* the capacitive reactance.

Why is this so?

As the frequency increases, the plates of the capacitor fill up and empty their charges faster and faster. As this happens it must necessarily follow that more current flows per unit of time as the frequency increases. If more current flows, it surely is an indication that resistance must have *decreased.* The decreased resistance is in the form of capacitive reactance.

An increase in capacitance — such as increasing the plate size, decreasing the distance between the plates, and so on — has a similar effect. Increased capacitance results in a decreased reactance.

When one compares resistance and capacitive reactance in the same circuit, he finds the effects are similar to those experienced with *inductive* reactance. There is one very important difference: capacitive reactance works in the opposite direction to inductive reactance.

What does this mean?

Again refer back to the voltage and current sine waves which occur whenever a resistance — pure ohmic resistance — is found alone in an a.c. circuit.

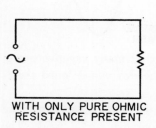

WITH ONLY PURE OHMIC
RESISTANCE PRESENT

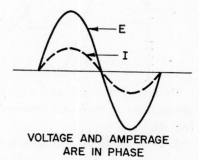

VOLTAGE AND AMPERAGE
ARE IN PHASE

In an a.c. circuit containing only pure ohmic resistance, voltage and amperage are *in phase.* They rise and fall together. They cross the zero reference line together. *True power* is exactly the same as *apparent power* . . . it is simply the product of E × I.

This is not true in a capacitive circuit. The current in a capacitive circuit does *not* begin to rise at the same instant that voltage rises. The voltage is delayed by an amount of time depending upon the capacitance the circuit possesses as compared to the amount of pure ohmic resistance.

If it were possible — which it is not — to have a circuit containing *only* capacitance, the voltage would be 90° out of phase with the amperage. At this point it might be wise to stop and recall that in a purely *inductive* circuit current lagged behind voltage by 90°. In a *capacitive* circuit current *leads* voltage by the same amount. One could express this latter phenomenon in another way: *In a capacitive circuit voltage lags current.*

To summarize, then, in an *inductive* circuit current *lags* behind voltage. In a *capacitive* circuit current *leads* voltage.

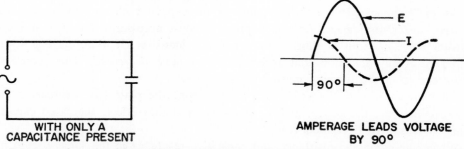

WITH ONLY A
CAPACITANCE PRESENT

AMPERAGE LEADS VOLTAGE
BY 90°

In a purely capacitive circuit, with amperage leading voltage by 90°, the true or useful power would be zero. This can be better understood if one again refers to a graph illustrating voltage, amperage, and power in a capacitive circuit.

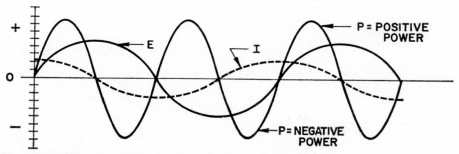

By referring to the above graph one can see there are as many *negative* power alternations as there are positive power alternations. The *true power* must therefore be *zero!*

It is a matter of fact that *some resistance is always present* in any capacitive circuit. Hence, some power is always available to accomplish useful work. The amount of true power available depends upon the relationship of capacitance to pure ohmic resistance.

206

THE RULE

If equal amounts of capacitive reactance and pure ohmic resistance are present the voltage and current are 45° out of phase. The voltage lags behind (current leads) by 45°.

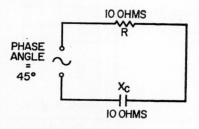

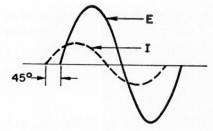

Review the Facts

1. In an alternating-current circuit having only pure ohmic resistance, voltage and amperage are *in phase*.
2. In a theoretical alternating-current circuit having only capacitive reactance, amperage leads voltage by 90°, and the true power is zero.
3. In an alternating-current circuit having equal amounts of pure ohmic resistance and capacitive reactance, current leads voltage by 45°.
4. Other phase angles from 0° to 90° are possible depending upon the amount of pure ohmic resistance in ratio to capacitive reactance, X_C. As the phase angle varies, the *true power* also varies, true power becoming less as the phase angle becomes greater.

The exact phase angle can always be calculated provided the pure ohmic resistance and the capacitive reactance are known. One of the simplest methods to make the computation is with the aid of a vector diagram.

An Example

Find the phase angle, and the *total* resistance of a circuit having the following amount of capacitive reactance and pure ohmic resistance:

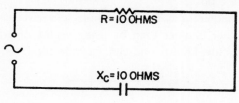

207

Procedure

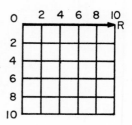

1. Using graph paper, or some kind of measuring device, lay off the vector R to a length of 10 units along a horizontal line.

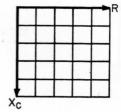

2. Using the same graph paper or measuring device, lay off X_C to a length of 10 units at right angles, downward, from the start of R.

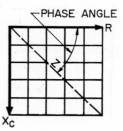

3. Complete a parallelogram, and draw a line diagonally from the intersection of R and X_C to the opposite corner. The diagonal line should be labeled with the letter Z.

    The phase angle is the angle between Z and R.

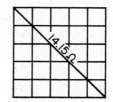

4. Diagonal line Z is also important because it represents "impedance." Impedance in this problem is the *total* resistance of R *and* X_C.

Z is the impedance line. It is the resultant of pure ohmic resistance and capacitive reactance. Measure it with the same units used for R and X_C to determine its ohmic value.

One cannot simply add R and X_C because of the phase angle which is involved. The two components must be treated with special mathematic methodology. Simple addition will not do!

One may wonder whether or not it is possible to arrive at the total a.c. resistance — Z — in any other manner than by using vector diagrams. The answer is "Yes." Once R and X_C are known one can find the total resistance by using the following formula:

$$Z = \sqrt{R^2 + X_C^2}$$

208

Example

Determine the total circuit resistance — *impedance* — for a circuit having 15 ohms of pure ohmic resistance, and 15 ohms of capacitive reactance.

Procedure:

1. State the formula: $Z = \sqrt{R^2 + X_C^2}$

2. Substitute in the formula: $Z = \sqrt{(15)^2 + (15)^2}$

3. Solve for the answer: $\sqrt{225 + 225} = \sqrt{450} =$
   21.21 ohms total impedance

REMEMBER·

Z = Impedance = Total Alternating Current Resistance

Once R, X_C, and Z are known *true power* can be calculated by using the following formula:

THE FORMULA

$$P_{TRUE} = E \times I \times \cos \Theta$$

$\cos \theta$ is the same as *power factor,* which is the ratio of resistance to impedance, or $\dfrac{R}{Z}$. $\cos \theta$ is *always less than 1* in an a.c. circuit having capacitance and pure ohmic resistance.

A Summary of Power Factor

The foregoing information regarding power factor may be summarized with a typical example.

Given: E = 200 volts
  I = 2 amperes
  R = 4 ohms
  X_C = 3 ohms
  Z = 5 ohms

Procedure:

1. Find $\cos \theta = \dfrac{R}{Z} = \dfrac{4}{5}$

2. Write the formula for true power: $P = E \times I \times P.F.$

3. Substitute and solve: $P = 200 \times 2 \times \dfrac{4}{5} = 320$ watts

Some Facts

1. *True power* is the power which is actually expended in accomplishing useful work. It varies with varying phase angles. It is the product of volts times amperes times cos θ.
2. *Apparent power* is the power which *appears* to be expended in accomplishing useful work. It is the simple product of volts times amperes.

   Apparent power does *not* take phase angle into consideration. In d.c. circuits apparent power is the same as true power because phase angle is not a factor which becomes involved, simply because amperage and voltage are always in phase in a direct-current circuit.
3. Power factor is the same as cos θ.
4. Cos θ is the same as the ratio of $\dfrac{R}{Z}$.
5. Power factor in a d.c. circuit is always equal to 1.
6. Power factor may be expressed either as a decimal or as a percentage. For example, a power factor of .75 may be expressed as 75%.

A Review

To review each of the concepts in its proper relationship to the whole, it is well to solve a problem completely through from its beginning. Using the schematic diagram below, find the values of the following: X_c, Z, p.f., true power, apparent power.

Procedure

1. Find X_C (capacitive reactance):

$$X_C = \frac{1}{2\pi f C} = \ ?$$

It is not necessary to find X_C because it is already given! If only capacitance had been given it would have been necessary to calculate capacitive reactance, and the above formula would have been used.

2. Find Z (impedance):

$$Z = \sqrt{R^2 + X_C^2} = \sqrt{(3)^2 + (4)^2} = \sqrt{9 + 16}$$
$$= \sqrt{25} = 5 \text{ ohms}$$

3. Find *p.f.* (power factor, or cos θ):

$$P.F. = \frac{R}{Z} = \frac{3}{5} = .60$$

4. Find true power:
   True Power $= E \times I \times P.F. = 100 \times 20 \times .60 = 1200$ watts
5. Find apparent power:
   Apparent Power $= E \times I = 100 \times 20 = 2000$ watts

Uses of Capacitive Reactance

Capacitive reactance is used to serve many useful purposes.

1. It is used in many electronic circuits as a block to direct current, but provides a "pathway" to alternating current.
2. It is used in motors to help provide the "revolving field" needed for capacitor-start a.c. motors.
3. It is used in radio and television tuning circuits, and as part of the power-supply network which helps smooth out unwanted ripples remaining after a.c. has been rectified.

Review the Facts

1. Capacitors block direct current, but permit alternating current to flow in an a.c. circuit.
2. Capacitive reactance is a form of resistance which is measured in ohms and represented by the symbol X_C.

   Capacitive reactance is equal to the reciprocal of: 6.28 times the frequency in cycles per second times capacitance in farads, or

   $$X_C = \frac{1}{2\pi \cdot f \cdot C}$$

3. Phase angle indicates the degree to which current *leads* voltage in a capacitive circuit.
4. Impedance is the *total* resistance in an alternating-current circuit. In an a.c. circuit having both pure ohmic resistance and capacitive reactance, one may find the total resistance — Z — by using the formula

   $$Z = \sqrt{R^2 + X_C^2}$$

   The letter Z is the symbol for impedance.
5. In an alternating-current circuit having one or more capacitors, an increase in frequency will *decrease* the capacitive reactance, and therefore decrease the total circuit resistance.
6. In an alternating-current circuit having one or more capacitors, an increase in capacitance will *decrease* the capacitive reactance, and therefore decrease the total circuit resistance.
7. The greater the capacitive reactance in an a.c. circuit, the more current will lead voltage, and the smaller will be the true power expended in the circuit. This is the same as saying that the greater the phase angle becomes the lesser is the true power.

211

8. Although it may seem that capacitive reactance is an unfortunate restricter of current, it is a fact that the world of electronics would be completely nonexistent without it. Capacitive reactance is used in motor operation, tuning circuits of radio and television, smoothing out unwanted ripples in electronic power-supply circuits, correcting undesirable power loss in an inductive circuit, and many other things.

REVIEW QUESTIONS

1. A coil of wire having an inductance of 10 henries, when plugged into a 60-cycle alternating-current voltage source, will have an inductive reactance of _____ ohms.

2. A coil of wire having an inductance of 10 millihenries, when plugged into a 100-cycle a.c. voltage source, will have an X_L of _____ ohms.

3. What will be the *total* resistance in a series a.c. circuit having a 30-ohm resistor, and a 40-ohm inductive reactance?

4. What will be the total resistance in a series *d.c.* circuit having a 100-ohm resistor, and a coil which has a pure ohmic resistance of 10 ohms and an inductive reactance of 6,280 ohms?

5. What will be the total resistance of an a.c. series circuit having a 3-ohm resistor, and a capacitor with a reactance of 4 ohms?

6. If a circuit has a 100-volt a.c. source, an amperage of 1 ampere, an impedance of 100 ohms, and a pure ohmic resistance of 60 ohms, what is the true power?

7. Which series circuit will have more total resistance:
   a) An a.c. circuit having a 10-ohm resistance, and a coil having 10 ohms of pure ohmic resistance and an X_L of 100 ohms;
   b) A d.c. circuit having the same components as above.

8. As the frequency increases in an inductive circuit the X_L (increases, decreases).

9. As the frequency increases in a capacitive circuit the X_C (increases, decreases).

10. Cosine θ, and the ratio of $\dfrac{R}{Z}$ are two expressions for _____ _____.

11. In a d.c. circuit *power factor* is always equal to 1. (True or false)

12. In an a.c. circuit *power factor* is always equal to 1. (True or false)

Unit 15

THE EFFECTS OF RESISTANCE, CAPACITANCE, AND INDUCTANCE

In Unit 14 the effects of resistance and inductance, and the effects of resistance and capacitance were explained. This unit explains how a.c. series and parallel circuits are affected when the parameters of resistance, inductance, and capacitance are all found within a single circuit.

A Review

In a circuit containing inductive reactance and pure ohmic resistance, impedance may be found using either one of two simple methods.

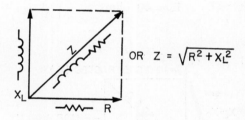

$$\text{OR} \quad Z = \sqrt{R^2 + X_L^2}$$

In a circuit containing capacitive reactance and pure ohmic resistance, impedance may be found using the same two methods used above.

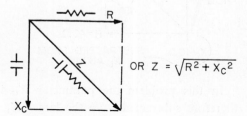

$$\text{OR} \quad Z = \sqrt{R^2 + X_C^2}$$

The two reactance formulas obviously work in opposite directions.

One can readily see this is true because the X_L formula employs simple multiplication of all terms. As frequency and inductance become greater, X_L becomes greater.

$$X_L = 2\pi F L$$

On the other hand, the X_C formula is a "reciprocal" type of formula. The greater frequency and capacitance become, the lower is X_C.

$$X_C = \frac{1}{2\pi F C}$$

The alert student readily recognizes that since the above statements are true, a point *may* be reached at which X_L cancels out X_C, and vice versa. How this happens, and the effects it has on series and parallel circuits, will be explored.

215

Series A.C. Circuits

Combining X_L and X_C With Vectors

$X_L = 30\,\Omega$
$X_C = 5\,\Omega$
$=$ $25\,\Omega$ X_L

The 5 ohms X_C subtracts from 30 ohms X_L, effectively leaving a 25-ohm X_L circuit.

$X_L = 10\,\Omega$
$X_C = 30\,\Omega$
$=$ $20\,\Omega$ X_C

The 10 ohms X_L subtracts from 30 ohms X_C, effectively leaving a 20-ohm X_C circuit.

Combining X_L, X_C, and R Using Vectors and Formulas

Given: $X_L = 50$ ohms
$X_C = 10$ ohms
$R = 40$ ohms

Find: Z (impedance)
Phase angle
Cos θ

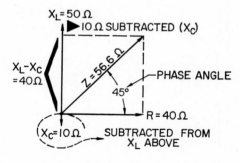

Whenever the three parameters of R, X_L, and X_C are found in one series circuit, resistance stands alone, and the smaller of reactance X_L or X_C is subtracted from the larger. The remaining reactance is then set up in a parallelogram with the resistance, R. Impedance, Z, is the resultant. The phase angle is that angle which results from the intersection of Z and R.

In this problem the parameter X_C is the smaller of the reactances, and is therefore subtracted from the larger X_L leaving a reactance of 40 ohms X_L. The parallelogram is then set up between the remaining 40 ohms of X_L and the 40 ohms of R. Measuring line Z yields an impedance of 56.6 ohms. Measuring the angle between Z and R yields a phase angle of 45°.

In the preceding problem, Cos θ can be found by dividing R by Z, thus:

$$\text{Cos } \theta = \frac{R}{Z} \quad or \quad \frac{40}{56.6} = .71$$

Using a Formula

The same problem could have been solved using a modification of the formula used in previous problems:

216

THE FORMULA

$$Z = \sqrt{R^2 + (X_L - X_C)^2}$$

Substitute values: $\sqrt{40^2 + (50 - 10)^2}$

Solve: $\sqrt{1600 + 1600} = \sqrt{3200} = 56.6$

Once Z and R are known, Cos θ can be found in the standard manner. The phase angle can be determined by referring to a table of trigonometric functions.

Another Problem

Given: $X_L = 15$ ohms
$X_C = 45$ ohms
$R = 20$ ohms

Find: Z (impedance)
Phase angle
Cos θ

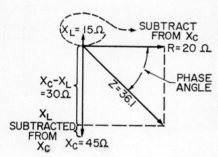

In this problem X_L is the smaller of the reactances, and it is therefore subtracted from the larger X_C, leaving an effective reactance of 30 ohms X_C. The parallelogram is then set up between the remaining 30 ohms of X_C and the 20 ohms of R. Measuring line Z yields an answer of 36.1 ohms impedance. Measuring the angle between Z and R yields a phase angle of 56°.

Power factor, or Cos θ, is solved by using the ratio of $\dfrac{R}{Z}$.

The preceding problem could have been solved by using the modified impedance formula:

$$Z = \sqrt{R^2 + (X_L - X_C)^2} = \sqrt{20^2 + (15 - 45)^2} = \sqrt{400 + 900}$$
$$= 36.1 \text{ ohms, impedance}$$

Reactance Values Not Given

It is wise to recall at this point that the past several problems dealing with X_L and X_C had the reactance values provided. It was not necessary to compute them.

Many problems provide only resistance, capacitance, and inductance. Before one can determine impedance it is necessary to compute X_L and X_C. To deter-

217

mine X_L one uses the formula $X_L = 2\pi \cdot f \cdot L$ by substituting inductance, in henries, for L. To determine X_C one uses the formula $X_C = \dfrac{1}{2\pi \cdot f \cdot C}$ by substituting capacitance, in farads, for C.

The values of X_L and X_C were provided in the previous problems to permit simplicity, which in turn provided clarity. Now that practice has been secured in the major concepts, the following problem takes an a.c. problem through from its very beginning, requiring the student to solve for all quantities, including X_L and X_C.

A Summary Problem

One might think to himself, "This is all very well, but what does it have to do with a real life situation? How do all of the foregoing bits of information fit together into a meaningful whole?"

An example, carried through from its beginning, will answer the above questions.

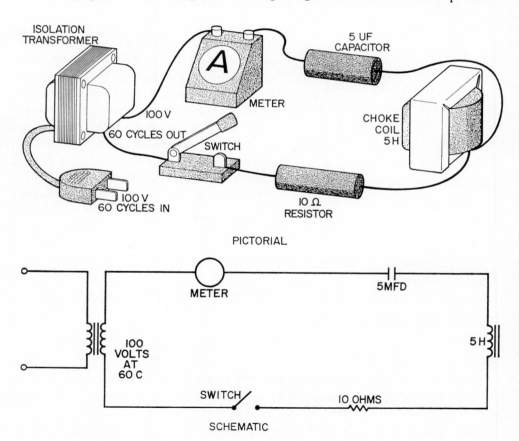

PICTORIAL

SCHEMATIC

Find: X_L, X_C, Z, I, E_R, E_L, E_C, E_T, Apparent power, True power.

Some Facts About the Problem

Since this is a series a.c. circuit there are some things one should already know about it without "working the problem."

1. *All* series circuits, both a.c. and d.c., have a current which is the same in all parts of the circuit. The current through R is exactly the same as through L and C at any given instant of time.

    All phase angles in a series a.c. circuit are measured with respect to the circuit current, not the circuit voltage. This is true because current is always the same throughout the circuit and therefore may serve as a dependable reference.

2. Voltage drops may vary around a series circuit, depending upon the resistance and current through any particular component. The higher the resistance of the component — either pure ohmic resistance or impedance — the higher is the voltage drop.

    In a d.c. series circuit the simple arithmetic sum of the voltage drops equals the source voltage. This is *not* true of an *a.c. series* circuit.

3. The voltage waveform across the pure ohmic resistance — R — is *in phase* with the current waveform.

4. The voltage waveform across the inductor — L — leads the current by 90°. This assumes that the inductor has no pure ohmic resistance at all. One should know by this time that the latter is not true, but it is assumed in order to permit a more clear handling of this problem.

5. The voltage waveform across the capacitor — C — lags behind the current by 90°. Again, this assumes the capacitor has no pure ohmic resistance present.

How to Attack the Problem

1. Find the reactances:
$$X_L = 2\pi f L = 6.28 \times 60 \times 5 = 1880 \text{ ohms}$$
$$X_C = \frac{1}{2\pi f C} = \frac{1}{6.28 \times 60 \times .000005} = 531$$

2. Find the impedance:
$$Z = \sqrt{R^2 + (X_L - X_C)^2} = \sqrt{(10)^2 + (1880 - 531)^2} = 1350 \text{ ohms}$$

3. Find the circuit current:
$$I = \frac{E}{Z} = \frac{100}{1350} = .074 \text{ ampere}$$

4. Find the voltage drop across each component:
    E_R (Voltage drop across resistor)
$$E_R = I_R \cdot R_R = .074 \times 10 = .74\text{-volt drop}$$
    E_L (Voltage drop across choke coil)
$$E_L = I_L \cdot X_L = .074 \times 1880 = 139\text{-volt drop}$$

E_C (Voltage drop across capacitor)

$$E_C = I_C \cdot X_C = .074 \times 531 = 39\text{-volt drop}$$

Here one should become concerned. Notice the sum of the voltage drops — 178 volts! *Fantastic!* When one considers the fact that the source voltage is only 100 volts, how can the sum of the voltage drops add to such a seemingly ridiculous figure?

This is one of the astonishing characteristics of alternating current.

If one were to *measure* the voltage drops with a voltmeter, he would find the meter's indication would be very nearly the same as the computed values.

Since all of this is true, it is not difficult to see that *apparent power* can differ from *true power* in an a.c. circuit. If one were to simply take the sum of the indicated voltage drops times the known circuit current, the apparent power — 132 watts — would be in error. And why?

Because of voltage lead and lag — the *phase relationship* — of *L* and *C*, true power cannot be found so simply.

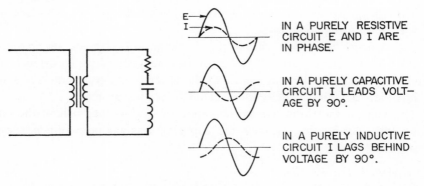

IN A PURELY RESISTIVE CIRCUIT E AND I ARE IN PHASE.

IN A PURELY CAPACITIVE CIRCUIT I LEADS VOLT-AGE BY 90°.

IN A PURELY INDUCTIVE CIRCUIT I LAGS BEHIND VOLTAGE BY 90°.

When one considers phase relationships, he understands that he can no more use simple addition to find the sum of the voltage drops, than he can dare use simple addition to find the sum of the resistance of *R, L,* and *C* which provides an answer in impedance.

No! The total voltage drop must be found by using the same methods used in finding *Z*.

Use of Vectors:

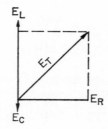

Where:

E_L = voltage drop across inductance
E_R = voltage drop across resistor
E_C = voltage drop across capacitor
E_T = *total* voltage drop

Use of Formulas:

$$E_T = \sqrt{E_R{}^2 + (E_L - E_C)^2}$$

220

When the individual voltage drops across R (E_R), across L (E_L), and across C (E_C) are handled either vectorially, or by formula, the total is the same as the source voltage!

5. To find the true power the formula $P = E \times I \times \cos \theta$ is used.
6. To find apparent power the formula $P = E \times I$ is used.

Resonance

Earlier in this unit it was stated that it would be possible, in an a.c. series circuit, to reach a point at which reactances X_C and X_L would cancel one another. This certainly can happen. Assume you have the following circuit with its associated values of pure ohmic resistance, voltage, and reactances.

Since X_C and X_L are both 50 ohms, and since both work in opposite directions to one another, they effectively cancel, and R is the only remaining resistance of any consequence.

It is a fact that X_L and X_C can be ignored so far as determining current and power are concerned. In this case current equals 5 amperes, and power is equivalent to 500 watts.

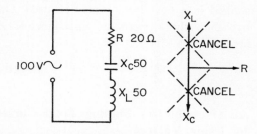

THE RULE

Resonance is that condition which exists when reactances cancel one another.

In a series A.C. circuit, current and power are at their greatest values when X_L and X_C are at a point of resonance.

In a series A.C. circuit, pure ohmic resistance is the only effective resistance present when X_L and X_C cancel one another.

The above concepts can be illustrated with the help of schematic diagrams:

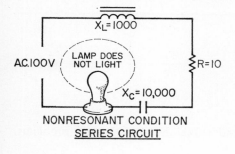

NONRESONANT CONDITION
SERIES CIRCUIT

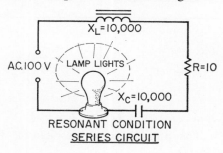

RESONANT CONDITION
SERIES CIRCUIT

Parallel A.C. Circuits

In direct-current parallel circuits the voltage drop across all branch resistors is equal. *The same is true of all a.c. parallel circuits.* What is more, the voltage measured across any, and all, of the branches, is equal to the source voltage, and all voltages are in phase. Thus, all phase angles in a parallel circuit are measured with respect to the circuit voltage unless otherwise indicated.

Current through a branch circuit depends upon the amount of resistance of that particular branch, and the voltage impressed upon it. Although the voltage phase angles are all in phase, the *current phase angles may vary anywhere from 0° to 90°.*

When computing total amperage, vectors and formulas similar to those already studied in series circuits, may be used. Once total circuit current has been found by using those methods, impedance — Z — can be determined by using the formula:

$$Z = \frac{E_T}{I_T} \quad or \quad \text{Impedance} = \frac{\text{Total voltage}}{\text{Total amperage}}$$

An Overview for Finding Total Current for Parallel A.C. Circuits by Using Vectors

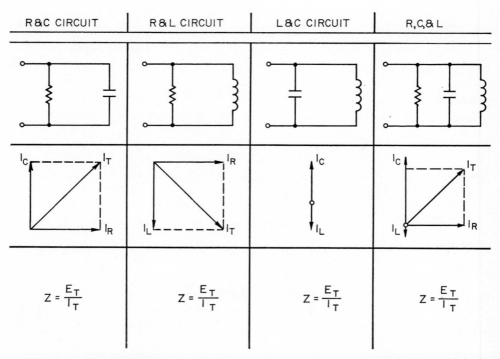

R & C CIRCUIT	R & L CIRCUIT	L & C CIRCUIT	R, C & L
$Z = \frac{E_T}{I_T}$	$Z = \frac{E_T}{I_T}$	$Z = \frac{E_T}{I_T}$	$Z = \frac{E_T}{I_T}$

The preceding concepts can be better understood by using actual problems.

Example 1

Given:

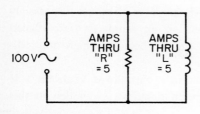

Find:

1. Total amperage (I_T)
2. Voltage drop across R (E_R)
3. Voltage drop across L (E_L)
4. Total voltage drop (E_T)
5. Total circuit resistance (Z)

Procedure:

1. Find I_T using vectors and formula.

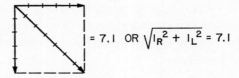

$= 7.1$ OR $\sqrt{I_R^2 + I_L^2} = 7.1$

2. Because this is a parallel circuit, the voltage drop across R is the same as the source voltage, or 100 v.
3. The voltage drop across X_L is the same as the source voltage, or 100 v.
4. The total voltage drop is the same as the source voltage because this is a parallel circuit, or 100 v.
5. Total circuit resistance $= Z = \dfrac{E_T}{I_T} = \dfrac{100}{7.1} = 14$ ohms.

From the above information, phase angle, Cos θ, true power, apparent power, and power factor may be found using the methods already studied.

Example 2

Given:

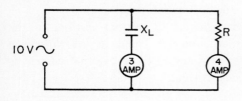

Find:

1. Total amperage $(I_T) = 5$ amperes
2. Total circuit resistance $(Z) = 2$ ohms

Example 3

Given:

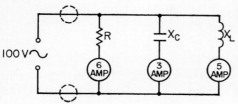

Find:

1. Total amperage $(I_T) = 6.32$ amperes
2. Total circuit resistance $(Z) = 15.82$ ohms

To provide an even keener understanding of the information shown in **No. 3** above, consider the following:

1. Since the computed total amperage is 6.32 amperes, it must necessarily follow that this amperage would be indicated if an ammeter were placed in series with the total circuit in either of the two places which are indicated with dotted lines in Example No. 3.

   At first this may seem strange. After all, in a parallel *d.c.* circuit, the total amperage is the sum of all of the branch circuits . . . which in this case would total to 14 amperes.

   But, this is *not* a d.c. circuit. It is an a.c. circuit! *And,* amperages in an a.c. circuit containing either X_C or X_L, or both, must be treated vectorially or with a special formula. Remember, in a *series* a.c. circuit, *voltage* could not simply be added, but instead had to be referred to vectors or special formula.

2. *Voltage drops* in an a.c. parallel circuit are treated the same as those in d.c. circuits.

Circulating Current

The past three examples dramatically indicate a phenomenon known as "circulating current." To investigate this mysterious concept even further, assume the following circuit exists.

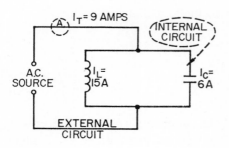

The circulating current is that current flowing within the *internal circuit.*

The current flowing through the capacitance is exactly opposite in polarity to the current flowing through the inductance, at any one instant of time.

The amount of current flowing in the external circuit is equal to the *difference* between I_C and I_L. The external current is the *line* current.

THE FORMULA

Line Current = $I_L - I_C$

In the example shown above the line current is 9 amperes. Since I_C is the smaller current it is said that I_C is the *circulating current.* The smaller current, whether it be I_C or I_L, is the circulating current.

Resonant A.C. Parallel Circuits

In a resonant a.c. parallel circuit, the current in the external circuit is theoretically *zero,* because the current within the internal circuit is as follows:

Within the internal circuit the inductor causes current to lag behind voltage by 90°, while the capacitor causes current to lead voltage by 90°. The two currents are thus 180° out of phase, and therefore cancel one another as they travel in opposite directions.

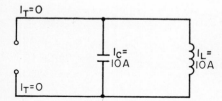

Theoretically there may be great currents flowing in the *internal* circuit, but zero current flowing in the external circuit.

All that would be required from the external circuit would be an instantaneous burst of current to get things going. After that the internal current would be self-sustaining.

As the initial burst of current goes through the inductor, a positive pole appears at one end, and a negative pole at the other. As the lines of force collapse, and the magnetic field withdraws toward the center of the loops of wire within the inductor, the polarities change.

The plates of the capacitor alternately load up and discharge in step with the inductor's changing polarity. Of course the capacitor's load, each time, is discharged through the inductor, thus keeping the latter operating.

All of this seems to be a form of perpetual motion, and indeed it would be if it were not for resistance. Resistance, like mechanical friction, prevents the condition from being truly self-sustaining. *Some resistance is always present.* However, the amount of current drawn from the source to overcome the pure ohmic resistance might be a very small amount — just enough to provide a "kick" to keep things going. The net result is the possibility of a relatively *high* current flowing in the internal circuit, but only a very small current flowing in the external circuit.

A practical circuit employing this very principle is known as a *tank circuit,* and is popularly used in the tuning circuits of radio transmitters and receivers.

In a transmitter the tuning circuit — tank circuit — determines the frequency at which the transmitter transmits its message.

In a radio receiver, the tank circuit determines the station that will be heard from the loudspeaker, and all others will be tuned out.

In a tank circuit the inductor or the capacitor may have a built-in feature which permits the inductance or capacitance to be varied. A variable inductor or capacitor permits changing the resonant frequency, thus changing the fre-

225

quency at which a transmitter sends its messages, or a radio receiver selects different stations.

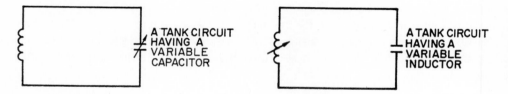

The condition described above might be diagramed as follows:

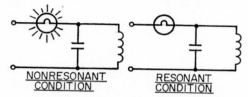

In a parallel circuit the light bulb may light provided the circuit is *not* resonant. On the other hand, it may light only dimly or not at all when the circuit is resonant. *This is the exact opposite of a series a.c. circuit.*

It is a fact that *total current* in a parallel circuit *cannot* be found by adding individual currents *directly*. The total current must be found vectorially, or by using appropriate formulas, much the same as total voltage was found in an a.c. series circuit.

In a combination $R, C,$ and L circuit, the *total* current flowing in the external circuit is the total of the current through the resistor (I_R) and the *difference* between the current through the inductor and capacitor (I_L and I_C). Furthermore, the *total* must be found by adding vectorially, *not* by simple addition: Thus:

THUS

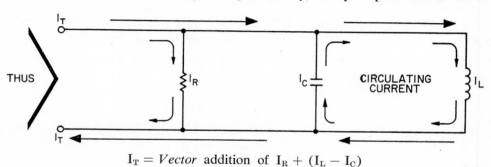

$$I_T = Vector \text{ addition of } I_R + (I_L - I_C)$$

Parallel impedance can then be found by substituting in a *modified* formula of Ohm's Law:

$$Z = \frac{E_T}{I_T}$$

The impedance formula can then be manipulated to provide other formulas, such as:

$$E_T = I_T Z \quad \text{and} \quad I_T = \frac{E_T}{Z}$$

Practical Circuits Employing Resistance, Inductance, and Capacitance

Resistance, capacitance, and inductance are not monsters to be feared, nor are they useless parameters which must be studied in order to practice useless mathematical formulas. To the contrary, they become very useful servants in many electronic applications.

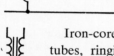

Tank circuits are used in citizens-band transceivers, radio and television receivers, radio station transmitters, and many other circuits.

Iron-core transformers are used for heating the filaments of vacuum tubes, ringing door bells, matching unlike impedances, for arc welders, power supplies, and thousands of other applications.

Air-core transformers, with associated capacitors, serve as tuned high-frequency couplers between amplifying stages in radio and television circuits.

Inductors and capacitors are sometimes used in circuits to smooth out the ripple left after rectifying alternating current to direct current.

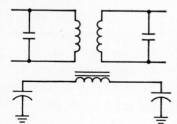

Some circuits which use inductors and capacitors permit only certain frequencies, or a single frequency, to pass while restricting the passage of others.

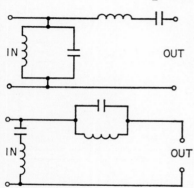

Other circuits employing inductance and capacitance filter out a single frequency or frequencies and prevent them from getting through from an input to an output.

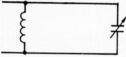

REVIEW QUESTIONS

1. A circuit having 30 ohms of inductive reactance, and 20 ohms of capacitive reactance will have an effective inductive reactance of _____ ohms.

2. A circuit having 30 ohms of inductive reactance, and 60 ohms of capacitive reactance will have an effective _____ reactance of _____ ohms.

3. A circuit having a pure ohmic resistance of 3 ohms, a capacitive reactance of 20 ohms, and an inductive reactance of 16 ohms, will have an impedance of _____ ohms.

4. A circuit having equal amounts of inductive reactance and pure ohmic resistance will have a phase angle of _____.

5. A circuit having equal amounts of capacitive reactance and pure ohmic resistance will have a phase angle of _____.

6. A circuit having equal amounts of capacitive reactance, inductive reactance, and pure ohmic resistance, will have a phase angle of _____.

7. A circuit having only inductive reactance, and no pure ohmic resistance or capacitive reactance, will have a phase angle of _____.

9. In an a.c. series circuit, (amperage, voltage) is always the same in all parts of the circuit for any given instant.

10. In an a.c. parallel circuit, (amperage, voltage) is always the same in all parts of the circuit.

11. The formula for apparent power is _____.

12. The formula for true power is _____.

13. A condition which results when inductive reactance cancels out capacitive reactance is called _____.

14. In a series a.c. circuit amperage is at its (maximum, minimum) when X_L and X_C are at a point of resonance.

15. In a parallel a.c. circuit amperage is at its (maximum, minimum) when X_L and X_C are at a point of resonance.

Unit 16

TRANSFORMERS

Direct current was the current first used in communities in the United States, and it was believed to be the best available at that time. When alternating current was proposed for residential and industrial use, people who had considerable money invested in d.c. fought against it. Mr. Thomas Edison was among the people who first failed to recognize the unique advantages of alternating current.

Persons like Mr. George Westinghouse and Mr. Nikola Tesla pointed out that alternating current could be changed from a high-amperage, low-voltage electricity to a high-voltage, low-amperage type, and again be reconverted. This latter fact was claimed to be an advantage when transporting electrical power over long distances.

Direct current could not be sent more than a few blocks from its generators because of the great voltage loss, and because large amperages would have required electrical wires larger in diameter than telephone poles. It is needless to point out the many insurmountable disadvantages of such an attempted operation.

On the other hand, alternating current could be transported hundreds of miles, over small wires, in the form of high voltage and low amperage. Once at its destination it could be stepped down to the needed low voltage and high available amperage.

Transformers permit the changing of voltage and amperage.

Water turbines and generators located at convenient damsites generate alternating current at about 6000 volts, step it up, with the aid of transformers, to 120,000 volts or more, transport it over wires to distant points, again step it down at substations to about 6000 volts for a city or village, and step it down once again at its final destination to about 220 volts for home and industrial use.

Once the stepped-down voltage has entered the home or laboratory, it can again be stepped up or down with the aid of smaller transformers which operate radios, television receivers, stereo amplifiers, power supplies, oscilloscopes, and thousands of other applications.

231

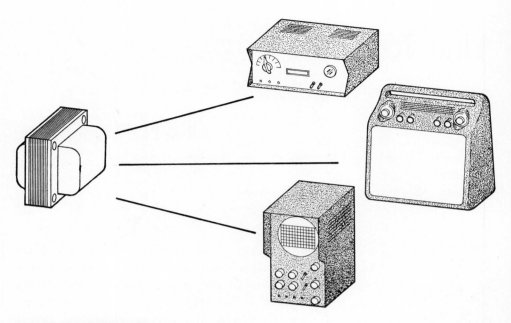

Principles of Operation

As alternating current flows through a coil of wire, expanding and contracting lines of magnetic flux cut across the windings of the coil. Whenever a wire, or windings of wire, are cut by magnetic flux lines, a voltage is induced into those windings. This is the principle upon which electric generators and inductors operate.

The *induced* voltage is exactly opposite — by 180° — to the *inducing* voltage. This phenomenon is known as Lenz's Law. Thus, in a coil of wire, the induced voltage is actually a back voltage, or a back e.m.f. (electromotive force) as it is often called. The process of inducing a back voltage into the *same* coil is known as *self-induction*.

There is also another kind of induction — *mutual induction* — which occurs when one coil of wire, which is connected to an a.c. source, is placed near a second coil of wire.

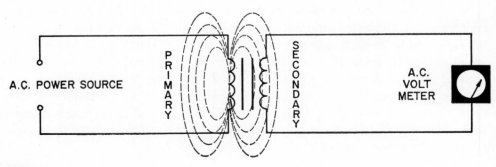

As the lines of force from the primary coil cut across the windings of the secondary coil, a voltage is induced into the secondary. When this happens, *mutual inductance* is taking place.

Transformers make use of mutual induction. A transformer has at least two windings of wire placed near one another. The two windings are physically insulated from one another, but magnetic flux lines electrically "couple" the two together.

It will be recalled from the unit on generators and motors, that the greater the number of turns of wire which are cut by magnetic flux lines, the greater is the induced voltage. To the contrary, the fewer the windings of wire cut by the flux lines, the lower is the induced voltage. This fact is used in designing transformers. It is this phenomenon which permits the construction of step-up and step-down transformers. The ratio of the number of turns of wire on the secondary, to those on the primary, determines the voltage which may be secured from the secondary.

Step-Down Transformers

This drawing shows a step-down transformer. There are 100 turns on the primary, and 10 turns on the secondary.

This is a ratio of 10 : 1.

When 120 volts are impressed upon the primary, 12 volts are available from the secondary.

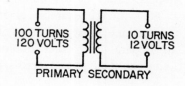

$$E_{SEC} = \frac{10}{100} \times 120 \text{ volts} = 12 \text{ volts}$$

Another factor comes to bear here. As the voltage is stepped *down*, amperage is automatically stepped up in like ratio. Thus, if one ampere is traveling through the primary, ten amperes are available at the secondary. Does this mean that ten amperes will actually flow from the secondary? Not necessarily! The amperage drawn from the secondary depends upon the resistance of the load connected across the secondary, and the voltage impressed upon the load by that same secondary winding.

Example

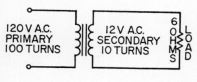

Using Ohm's Law in this case, one finds that 2 amperes flow from the secondary because only 2 amperes can get through a circuit having 12 volts, and a load resistance of 6 ohms.

$$I = \frac{E}{R} = \frac{12}{6} = 2 \text{ amperes}$$

233

Although 10 amperes were *available* at the secondary, only two amperes were present because of the load resistance.

Step-Up Transformers

This drawing shows a step-up transformer. There are 100 turns on the primary, and 1000 turns on the secondary. Again the ratio happens to be 10 to 1, but this time it is in a step-up direction.

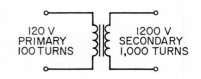

120 V
PRIMARY
100 TURNS

1200 V
SECONDARY
1,000 TURNS

When 120 volts are impressed upon the primary, 1200 volts are available at the secondary.

$$E_{SEC} = \frac{1000}{100} \times 120 = 1200 \text{ volts a.c.}$$

What was true of amperage in the step-down transformer is also true of amperage in the step-up transformer. *But,* in the step-up transformer amperage is stepped *down* in like ratio.

Thus, in the example given, if the maximum amperage in the primary is 1 ampere, the most amperage which may be drawn from the secondary is $\frac{1}{10}$ of an ampere. The exact amount of amperage taken from the secondary depends upon the load placed across its terminals.

THE RULE

The POWER drawn from the secondary can never exceed the power in the primary.

If it were possible to secure more power (wattage) from the secondary than goes into the primary, one would be getting something for nothing. This is contrary to the laws of physics. It is not possible.

Power is transferred from primary to secondary. Power is not generated by a transformer. Secondary power can never be greater than the power in the primary.

THE FORMULA

$$E_p I_p = E_s I_s$$

$$P_{PRIMARY} = P_{SECONDARY}$$

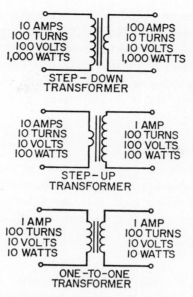

10 AMPS
100 TURNS
100 VOLTS
1,000 WATTS

100 AMPS
10 TURNS
10 VOLTS
1,000 WATTS

STEP-DOWN
TRANSFORMER

10 AMPS
10 TURNS
10 VOLTS
100 WATTS

1 AMP
100 TURNS
100 VOLTS
100 WATTS

STEP-UP
TRANSFORMER

1 AMP
100 TURNS
10 VOLTS
10 WATTS

1 AMP
100 TURNS
10 VOLTS
10 WATTS

ONE-TO-ONE
TRANSFORMER

The terms *step-up and step-down,* and *one-to-one* refer to *voltage.* It is understood that amperage works in a direction *opposite* to voltage.

Transformer Losses

Although many transformers are nearly 100 percent efficient, permitting almost as much wattage to be drawn from the secondary as is put into the primary, there are some losses which must be considered. Two of the most common are: (1) core losses, and (2) copper losses.

Core losses, in turn, may be divided into two categories: (1) eddy currents, and (2) hysteresis.

The same magnetic flux lines which cut across the secondary windings also cut across the core, a ferrous metal. The result is the induction of currents — eddy currents — in the core, which in turn cause heat. Increasing the resistance of the core material limits the flow of current in the core, and thereby reduces the power loss. Using thin sheets of a special iron alloy, covered with varnish, limits the cross section of each iron core piece, and therefore limits the eddy currents and ensuing power loss. The core materials thus constructed are called *laminations.*

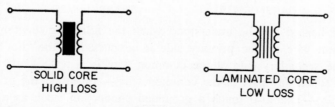

SOLID CORE
HIGH LOSS

LAMINATED CORE
LOW LOSS

Hysteresis losses are due to the kind of material used in the core. Certain elements, or alloys of elements, produce less hysteresis loss than other. Silicon steel is such a material, and it is often used in transformer laminations.

Copper losses occur from the resistance of the copper wire windings. Current flow heats the windings, and the heat is dissipated wastefully into the surrounding air. Heat is power which can be calculated with the formula, I^2R. I is the amperage through the coil, and R is the resistance of the wire. The answer is in watts.

Multivoltage Transformers

A transformer may have more than one voltage available at the secondary. It is possible to have a step-up, and a step-down transformer inside one frame. This is accomplished by having more than one winding on the secondary. Each winding has its own turns ratio as compared with the primary.

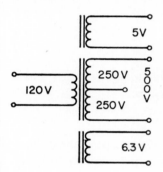

The schematic diagram shown here represents a common power transformer. Several voltages are available at the secondary: 5 volts, 6.3 volts, and a center-tapped 500-volt winding which provides 250 volts on either side of the center tap.

The Autotransformer

Autotransformers have only one winding. One wire of the autotransformer is *common* to both the "primary" and "secondary" winding. The advantage of this type of device is its relatively inexpensive construction. Its disadvantage lies in the fact that the primary is not physically isolated from the secondary winding, thus making the device potentially dangerous for shock hazard.

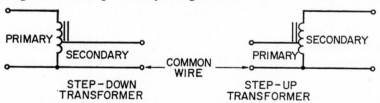

The shock hazard can be understood when the following diagram is studied. If the common wire on the primary side is connected to the "hot" side of the *main* line, the secondary side of the common wire is also "hot." If one were to inadvertently touch any part of the common wire — on either the primary *or* the secondary side — and also touch a grounded connection, such as a water pipe, he could be electrocuted.

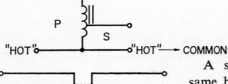

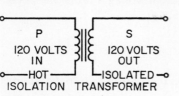

"HOT"○──────────────○"HOT"──→ COMMON

TOUCHING THE "HOT"–COMMON–
WIRE OF AN AUTOTRANSFORMER, AND
ALSO TOUCHING A GROUNDED OBJECT
CAN RESULT IN SHOCK HAZARD.

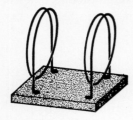

P | S
120 VOLTS IN | 120 VOLTS OUT
○──HOT──── | ──ISOLATED──○
ISOLATION TRANSFORMER

A standard transformer does not pose the same hazard because the secondary is physically isolated from the primary. Hence, such a transformer is sometimes called an *isolation* transformer, and may be used to prevent shock hazard when working with so-called "grounded chassis" equipment, which is dangerous to handle when plugged *directly* into an a.c. outlet.

Many standard transformers have a simple 1-to-1 ratio, with no step-up or step-down voltages. Its sole function is to isolate the primary from the secondary.

Specialized Transformers

There are many specialized transformers used throughout the world of electronics. Some of these are described below.

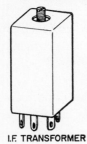

R.F. TRANSFORMER

Radio-frequency (r.f.) *transformers,* often used in transmitters, usually contain few turns of wire, and have an air core rather than an iron core.

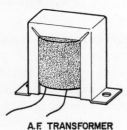

I.F. TRANSFORMER

Intermediate-frequency (i.f.) *transformers,* used in radio and television receivers, may have an air core, or they may have a powdered-iron slug which can be moved in and out of the coil effectively to change the inductance of the transformer, and therefore change its inductive reactance.

A.F. TRANSFORMER

Audio-frequency (a.f.) *transformers* are designed for relatively low frequencies within the audio range, usually considered to be from about 30 to about 15,000 cycles per second. They contain silicon-iron cores, and their inductive reactance is relatively high. They are many times used for output transformers, coupling high-impedance vacuum tubes to low-impedance speaker voice coils.

237

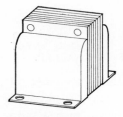

POWER TRANSFORMER

Power transformers are used in many industrial and domestic applications. These transformers are very often used to provide several different voltages from the secondary windings.

Pure direct current *cannot be transformed!* If direct current is to be stepped up or down with transformers, it must be varied, sending *pulsating direct current* to the primary winding.

Alternating current, of course, may be transformed.

Why is this so?

Because the primary must have expanding and contracting lines of flux *cutting* across the secondary windings. Then, and only then, can a voltage be induced into the secondary. Pure direct current does not provide this expansion and contraction of a magnetic field. Thus, no windings are cut by the magnetic field produced by pure direct current except for the momentary surge produced when the switch is first closed, and the collapse of the steady magnetic field as the switch is again opened.

REMEMBER
Only pulsating direct current and alternating current can be transformed to higher or lower voltages.

Transformers can change pulsating direct current to a.c., but they cannot change alternating current to d.c.

Connecting Transformers

Transformers may be connected in series or parallel in much the same manner that batteries or other power supplies can be coupled together in order to secure a higher amperage or voltage.

It will be recalled from the first units of this textbook that batteries may be connected in series to secure higher voltages. Connecting them in parallel provides higher available amperages. Transformers may be treated in the same manner.

Connecting the secondary windings of transformers in series provides higher voltages. Connecting the secondaries in parallel provides higher available amperages. Preferably the transformers being coupled together should individually have the same voltage and amperage ratings.

Connecting transformer secondaries in series *adds* voltages. Amperage remains the same as that which would be available from each individual transformer.

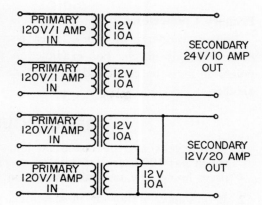

Connecting transformer secondaries in parallel *adds* amperage. The output voltage remains the same as that which would be available from each individual transformer.

A Word of Caution

In order to connect transformer secondaries together properly, the polarity of both secondaries *must be the same.* For example, if one were to connect two secondaries in series in order to add voltages, the windings of both transformers would have to be wound in corresponding directions, or the total voltage would be *less* than that of either transformer, rather than being additive. In the examples shown below both transformers are wired in series, but the schematic B has the transformers wired "backwards." It is a simple matter to determine whether the secondaries have been connected correctly. After the hookup is made, a voltmeter check will readily disclose an improper connection — a voltage indication *less* than the output of either secondary proves the connection has been improperly made.

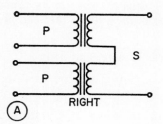

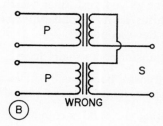

In the examples shown below an attempt has been made to wire both transformers in parallel, but schematic B is incorrect — a short exists! The transformer windings in B would burn out provided the primary was not properly fused.

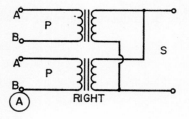

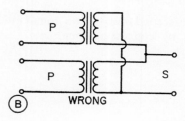

Primary Connections

Primary windings, of course, must also be connected in such a manner that their polarities match. For example, in the parallel connection shown above, points *A* must be connected together, and points *B* must be connected to one another.

REVIEW QUESTIONS

1. If 100 volts a.c. are connected into the primary winding of a transformer which has 1000 turns of wire on its primary, and 10,000 turns on its secondary, how many maximum volts can be secured from the secondary?

2. If 1 ampere is flowing in the primary winding of a transformer which has 1000 turns of wire on its primary, and 10,000 turns on its secondary, how much maximum amperage can be secured from the secondary?

3. If 100 watts are the maximum power which can be found in the primary winding of a transformer which has 1000 turns of wire on its primary, and 10,000 turns on its secondary, what is the maximum wattage that can be secured from the secondary?

4. If 100 volts a.c. are connected into the primary winding of a transformer which has 1000 turns of wire on its primary, and 100 turns on its secondary, how many maximum volts can be secured from the secondary?

5. If 1 ampere is flowing in the primary winding of a transformer which has 1000 turns of wire on its primary, and 100 turns on its secondary, how much maximum amperage can be secured from the secondary?

6. If 10 watts are the maximum power which can be found in the primary winding of a transformer which has 1000 turns of wire on its primary, and 100 turns on its secondary, what is the maximum wattage that can be secured from the secondary?

7. R.f. transformers usually have _____ turns of wire, and a/an _____ core.

8. A.f. transformers usually have a/an _____ core, and are used in a lower frequency range than r.f. transformers.

9. Pulsating d.c. and a.c. may be stepped up or down in a transformer, but _____ _____ _____ may never be transformed.

10. A type of transformer which can produce a shock hazard is the _____.

11. Isolation transformers having a 1-to-1 ratio are used to prevent _____ _____.

12. The secondaries of two transformers may be connected in order to add voltage by connecting them in _____.

Unit 17

RECTIFICATION

Many hundreds of applications require direct current for their operation. Among these are battery chargers, electroplaters, radio receivers, television, stereo amplifiers, and transistorized equipment.

Since more than 99 percent of the electrical energy supplied by electric light and power companies is alternating current, it is obvious some means must be available for changing a.c. to d.c.

In the past many methods for changing alternating current to direct current have been used, including the employment of vacuum tubes. Today, solid-state electronics has opened the door to efficient rectification believed impossible just a few years ago. Solid-state rectifiers can produce many times the amperage which can be delivered by a much larger vacuum tube. This unit deals with the most important aspects of rectification, but it is limited to the types of rectifiers which are most popular today, and promise to be the outstanding rectifying devices of tomorrow — the solid-state diodes.

EXAMPLES OF THE SILICON DIODE AND THEIR UNIVERSAL SCHEMATIC SYMBOL

What Is Rectification?

Rectification refers to the changing of alternating current to direct current. It results in current flow in one direction, rather than the flow of current in two directions. Rectification can best be illustrated in graph form:

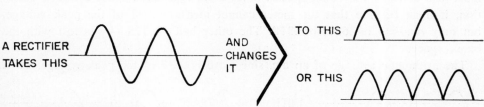

A RECTIFIER TAKES THIS

AND CHANGES IT

TO THIS

OR THIS

What Is a Rectifier?

A rectifier is a device which has a very high resistance to the flow of current in one direction, but a low resistance to the flow of current in the opposite direction.

243

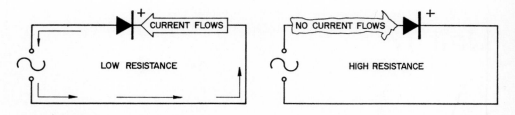

Half-Wave Rectification

Half-wave rectification results whenever a single diode rectifier is placed in series with an alternating-current circuit. The illustration below shows such a circuit connected to a load resistor, and an oscilloscope which shows the resultant pulsating direct-current pattern.

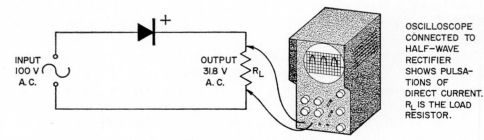

OSCILLOSCOPE CONNECTED TO HALF−WAVE RECTIFIER SHOWS PULSATIONS OF DIRECT CURRENT. R_L IS THE LOAD RESISTOR.

If one observes the pattern on the oscilloscope, it is obvious that one entire pulsation has been cut away from the original wave form. This, in turn, should make it clear that if a meter is connected to the circuit instead of the oscilloscope, the full voltage impressed upon the circuit by the a.c. source certainly will not be available at the output.

Since a meter responds to the *average* voltage it might seem that a meter reading would be equal to the arithmetic average, or .637 of the peak voltage. This is not true.

Notice there is a pulsation of direct current, then a blank space, another pulsation, and so on. It is true that a meter responds to an average voltage, but it must also consider the blank spaces. Since there is a blank space for each pulsation, it must be true that the meter cannot measure .637 of the peak voltage, but only *one-half* of .637, or .318. The other half — .318 — was lost with the blank space.

The arithmetic average of an a.c. sine wave is .637 of the peak voltage.

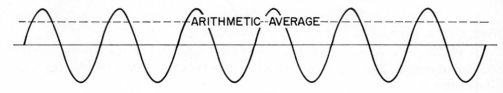

A half-wave rectifier cuts away one alternation of the incoming a.c. sine wave. A d.c. meter measuring the resulting pulsations indicates one-half of .637, or .318 of the peak voltage.

Full-Wave Rectification

Rectifiers can be connected in such a manner that the full .637 of the peak voltage can be secured. One such method, and a very popular one, is called the *bridge rectifier circuit*. It is a full-wave rectifier which does not cut off the bottom a.c. alternation, but instead moves it up above the zero reference line. Study the diagram below.

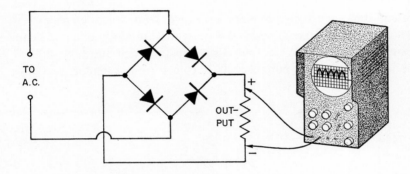

How is full-wave rectification accomplished? One can more easily understand the action by again referring to diagrams.

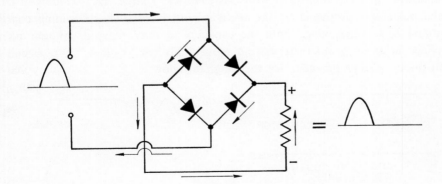

During one alternation, current flows in the direction of the arrows and produces one pulsation of direct current.

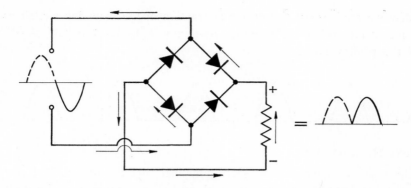

During the next alternation, current flows in the direction of the arrows and produces the second pulsation of direct current. And so on and on and on, alternation after alternation, pulsation after pulsation.

Filters

Pulsating direct current produces excessive hum when connected to audio (sound) circuits. In other circuits the pulsations produce other difficulties. For these purposes the "ripple" of pulsating direct current must be filtered out to make it more nearly like pure d.c. as it comes from a battery.

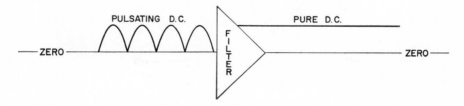

How Filtering Is Accomplished

A capacitor has the ability to store an electrical charge. By so doing it can take the pulsations produced by the rectifier, and store each succeeding charge (pulsation) that comes along until the capacitor is fully charged. At that point the voltage is at its peak, there are no more "hills" or "valleys," but instead a smooth direct current prevails. See the diagram below.

RECTIFIER OUTPUT
+
CAPACITOR = ZERO

CAPACITOR ADDED TO RECTIFIER

As each succeeding pulsation comes along the plates of the capacitor take on a charge, smoothing out the hills and valleys of the pulsating d.c.

246

At this point all would be well, and the direct current produced by the rectifier and its associated filter capacitor might be used, except for one thing. As a load is placed across the capacitor, an amount of current flows depending upon the demand of the load. The greater the demand, the higher the amperage.

As an amperage is drawn from the capacitor, the incoming pulsations cannot keep the capacitor filled with a full charge, and ripples again appear. True, the ripples are not as bad as they would be without the capacitor, but they are too great for many electronic applications.

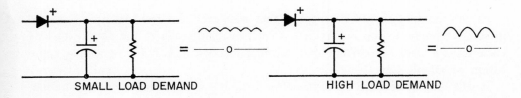

SMALL LOAD DEMAND   HIGH LOAD DEMAND

Adding a Resistance and Second Capacitor

By adding a resistor to the circuit, in series to ground with a second capacitor, the ripple can be almost completely eliminated even though a load is connected to the circuit.

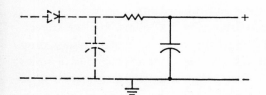

Added components reduce ripple to a minimum.

How do the new components act to help further reduce ripple?

The ripple coming from the power supply is called a.c. *component*. A.c component differs from true a.c. in that it never goes below the zero reference line. Nevertheless it has many of the characteristics of alternating current, even though it is d.c. Study the following illustration.

0 ——⟋\⟍—— = TRUE A.C.   0 ——————— = A.C.
COMPONENT

It will be noted that the a.c. component is relatively small in value as compared with the distance it is located above the zero reference line. In other words, the a.c. component *voltage* is *small* compared with the d.c. upon which it is riding.

247

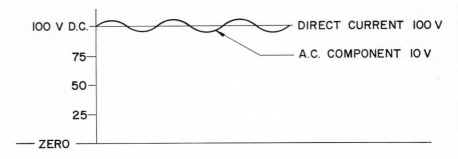

100 V D.C.

DIRECT CURRENT 100 V

A.C. COMPONENT 10 V

75—

50—

25—

— ZERO —

At this point it should be recalled that whenever two resistors are connected in series, a voltage drop occurs across each in relationship to the ohmic value of each resistor, and the current flow through the two is $E = I\,R$, a simple application of Ohm's Law.

It will also be recalled that capacitors exhibit a type of resistance to alternating current which is called "capacitive reactance," or X_C. Carbon resistors, of course, contain pure ohmic resistance. Also, one should remember that a carbon resistor passes *both* a.c. and d.c., but a capacitor permits *only* a.c. to "pass."

Connecting the added resistor and capacitor in series causes a voltage drop across each which is proportional to the resistance of each component. No d.c. can be dropped across the capacitor because no direct current can get through. Only a.c. voltage can be dropped across the added capacitor.

Assume the resistor has a pure ohmic resistance of 100 ohms, and the capacitor has a capacitive reactance of 1000 ohms. Ten times as much voltage drop occurs across the capacitor as across the resistor. Since the capacitor is in series with the resistor, and since the capacitor *does* permit alternating current to flow, 10 times as much a.c. component is dropped across the capacitor (and from there to ground) than is dropped across the resistor. Thus, the vast majority of the a.c. component is dropped across the capacitive reactance of the output capacitor, and led harmlessly to ground. Because d.c. cannot get through the capacitor there is no d.c. voltage drop across that component. True, a d.c. voltage drop does occur across the resistor, but it is a very small amount, leaving most of the direct current available to be used by the load. The net result is a power supply, and filter network which produces an almost pure direct current.

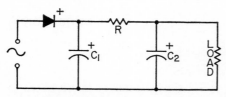

Capacitor C_1 helps smooth out d.c. as it comes from the rectifier. C_2, which is in series to ground with R, has a high X_C which causes a high a.c. voltage drop, thus eliminating any remaining a.c. component.

This type of filter is sometimes known as a "pi" filter, and it is the most popular of all the many different types. Electrolytic capacitors are usually used in the pi filter because they possess the necessary high capacitance rating, and they can be built into a relatively small container.

Using Chokes

In more expensive power supplies, chokes are often used in place of resistors. Chokes are simply windings of wire wound upon a laminated iron core, similar in construction to transformers. Although considerably more expensive than resistors, chokes are more efficient than their counterparts because of the fact that they have a much higher resistance to a.c., and to a.c. component, than they have to pure d.c. This latter characteristic is true because of the fact that chokes contain both pure ohmic resistance *and* inductive reactance to the passage of a.c., but oppose d.c. with only pure ohmic resistance. This latter principle can easily be reviewed by referring to Unit 15.

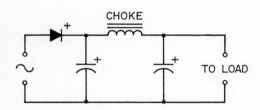

Chokes are sometimes used in place of resistors. Chokes have a higher *total* resistance to a.c. than to d.c., thus helping to eliminate undesirable a.c. component while permitting d.c. to be delivered to the load.

Voltage Output

After alternating current has been rectified and properly filtered, it is found that the output voltage is neither .318, nor .637. Indeed, it is nearer to the peak voltage value of the a.c. input. A very desirable and efficient outcome.

Voltage Dividers

If one wished to have a single output voltage, either the half-wave or full-wave rectifier with its filter circuit would be adequate. However, if more than one output voltage is needed, some means must be devised in order to secure the necessary voltages from a single source. The latter can be accomplished by using a voltage divider.

A voltage divider can be either a fixed resistor with taps at different points, or it can be a variable resistor capable of producing a variety of voltages.

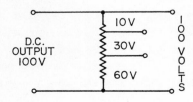

A power supply having its d.c. output connected to a tapped resistor can supply as many different voltages as there are taps at different points on the fixed resistor.

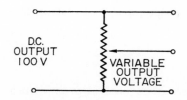

DC. OUTPUT 100 V

VARIABLE OUTPUT VOLTAGE

A power supply having its d.c. output connected to a variable resistor, such as a potentiometer, can supply a varying voltage output depending upon the position of the potentiometer arm.

REVIEW QUESTIONS

1. Draw a schematic diagram showing a half-wave rectifier with a pi filter, and a variable-resistance voltage divider.

2. Draw a schematic diagram showing a bridge circuit full-wave rectifier, with a pi filter, and a tapped fixed resistor voltage divider.

3. Draw a wave-form diagram illustrating half-wave pulsating direct current.

4. Draw a wave-form diagram illustrating full-wave pulsating direct current.

5. Draw a wave-form diagram illustrating a.c. component riding on top of a direct current.

GLOSSARY

Ammeter — An electrical instrument used for measuring current flow, in units of amperes.

Apparent Power — The product of volts × amperes, in units of watts. Apparent power does not reflect the effects of reactance on a.c. circuits.

Atoms — The smallest particle of matter which can exist and retain its identity as an element.

Autotransformer — A transformer having a primary winding which is also part of the secondary winding.

Battery — Two or more cells connected in series or parallel, or series/parallel.

C. E. M. F. — Counter electromotive force. A back voltage, or a back pressure.

Capacitance — Opposition to a change in voltage.

Capacitive Reactance — The opposition offered by a capacitor to the flow of alternating current. Represented by the symbol X_C. Measured in ohms.

Capacitor — An electrical component used for storing an electrical charge.

Conductor — Matter having a plentiful supply of free electrons.

Coulomb — A quantity of electrons equal to 6,280,000,000,000,000,000 or 6.28×10^{18}.

Current — A flow of amperage or electrons.

Eddy Current — The current induced into conductive materials by varying magnetic fields.

Electrolyte — A conducting liquid capable of passing an electric current.

Electrons — Negatively charged particles found in the outer shell or shells of atoms.

Farad — A unit of capacitance.

Frequency — The number of cycles per second of an alternating current.

Galvanometer — An electrical instrument used for measuring very small values of amperage or current flow.

Generator — A machine used for converting mechanical energy into electrical energy.

Hysteresis — The tendency of a material to retain magnetism, and to oppose a change in magnetism, thus resulting in energy loss.

Impedance — The total opposition of a circuit or component to alternating current. The vectorial sum of resistance and reactance. Represented by the symbol Z.

Inductance — The property of a component or circuit to oppose any change in current flow.

Inductive Reactance — The opposition offered by an inductor to the flow of alternating current. Represented by the symbol X_L. Measured in units of ohms.

Inductor — A coil.

Insulator — Matter having few or no free electrons.

Ion — An atom which has either lost or gained electrons. A "charged" atom.

Joule — A unit of work.

Kirchhoff's First Law — The current entering a circuit equals the current leaving.

Kirchhoff's Second Law — The sum of the voltage drops around a circuit equals the voltage applied across the circuit.

Molecule — The building blocks of matter containing two or more different elements.

Motor — A machine used for converting electrical energy into mechanical energy.

Node — The junction of two or more resistors or circuits.

Ohm — A unit of resistance.

Ohm's Law — Mathematical relationship of voltage, amperage, and resistance.

Ohmmeter — An electrical instrument for measuring resistance in units of ohms.

Parameter — A variable which can be used to help determine other variables. A changing quantity. Examples are voltage, amperage, resistance.

Polarization — Result of hydrogen bubbles forming at the pole of a battery or cell.

Power Factor — A percentage rating, or decimal fraction, secured by dividing resistance by impedance. The same as cosine theta.

Primary Cell — A voltage source incapable of being "recharged." Incorrectly called a "dry cell."

Primary Winding — The winding of a transformer which is connected to a power source. The input winding.

Protons — Positively charged particles found in the center, or nucleus of an atom.

Reactance — The opposition to the flow of alternating current, caused by the capacitance of a capacitor, or by the inductance of a coil, or both, measured in units of ohms.

Rectification — The process of changing alternating current to direct current.

Rectifier — A component used for changing alternating current to pulsating direct current.

Relay — An electro-mechanical switch.

Resistance — The opposing action that limits or controls the flow of electrons.

Resonance — A condition which exists when inductive reactance is equal to, and cancels capacitive reactance.

Secondary Cell — A voltage source capable of being "recharged." Sometimes referred to as a "wet" cell or "storage battery."

Secondary Winding — The winding of a transformer which is connected to a load. The output winding.

Shunt — A parallel connection, such as a resistance connected in parallel with another component, or one winding of a motor connected in parallel with another winding.

Time Constant — The time required to charge a capacitor to 63.2% of its total possible charge.

Transformer — Two or more coils usually designed in such a manner as to step-up or step-down a voltage, while changing amperage in a direction opposite to voltage.

True Power — The effective power in an electrical circuit, measured in units of watts. The product of volts × amperes × power factor.

Voltage — Electrical force, electrical pressure, E., V., E.M.F.

Voltage Divider — A resistor with fixed or movable taps, or a variable resistor, used to secure various voltages from a constant source voltage.

Watt — A unit of electrical power.

ANSWERS TO
REVIEW QUESTIONS

UNIT 1, page 8

1. Salt, pepper, sugar, wood, candy, radios, animals, people, water, milk, etc.

2. Atoms are tiny building blocks of matter made of only one kind of matter which is called an element.

3. Carbon, aluminum, copper, iron, lead, zinc, oxygen, hydrogen, helium, neon, etc.

4.

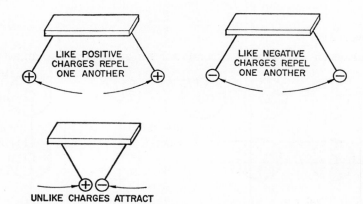

5.
or

or any other combinations having electrons outnumbering protons, or vice versa.

6. Same as No. 5.

7. Like charges repel, unlike charges attract.

8.

9.

10. Ten coulombs of electrons flowing past a given point in 1 second is the same as 10 amperes.

11. A coulomb is a *quantity* of electricity. An ampere is a *flow* of coulombs in a given unit of time.

12. Ampere = amp., or *I;* Coulomb = *Q;* Time = *t*

13. Matter having few or no free electrons.

14. Matter which has a plentiful supply of free electrons.

15.

UNIT 2, page 19

1. Voltage is the potential, pressure, or "push" that forces electrons along a conductor.

2.

(+5) ←———— (−5)

3. *A* is (higher ~~lower~~) than *B*
   A is (higher ~~lower~~) than *C*
   B is (higher ~~lower~~) than *D*
   B is (~~higher~~ lower) than *A*
   C is (~~higher~~ lower) than *A*
   C is (higher ~~lower~~) than *D*
   C is (~~higher~~ lower) than *B*
   C is (higher ~~lower~~) than *E*
   D is (~~higher~~ lower) than *A*
   D is (higher ~~lower~~) than *E*
   E is (~~higher~~ lower) than *C*
   E is (~~higher~~ lower) than *A*

4. There is a +5 volt drop from *A* to *C*, or *C* to *E*.
   There is a −5 volt drop from *C* to *A*, or *E* to *C*.
   There is a −1 volt drop from *C* to *B*, or *D* to *C*.
   There is a +6 volt drop from *A* to *D*, or *B* to *E*.

5. V, E, EMF, electromotive force, pressure, potential

UNIT 3, page 30

1. A liquid which will serve as a conductor for an electric current.

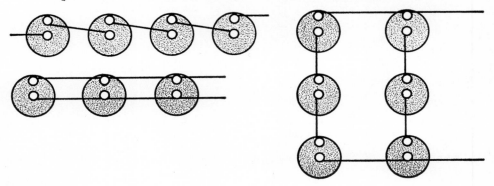

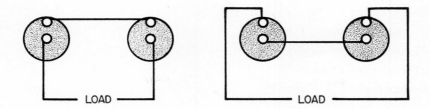

LOAD   LOAD

UNIT 4, page 40

1. Resistance is an opposing action that limits, controls, or holds back current.
2. Decreases
3. Increases
4. Poor conducting material; greater length; smaller cross-sections area; higher temperature.
5. Ohm
6. R or Ω
7. ⌇⌇⌇
8. Toasters, flat irons, electric light bulbs, radios, TV, electric horn, dishwasher, electric stove, clothes washer, clothes dryer, etc.
9. Black, brown, red, orange, yellow, green, blue, violet gray, white
10. 1000; 2200; 27,000 plus or minus 10%; 680,000 plus or minus 5%
11. 1000; 5600; 19,000; 47,000
12. Because resistors vary somewhat from the indicated value. The tolerance band indicates the maximum amount the resistor may vary.
13. 900–1100 ohms
14. 950–1050 ohms

UNIT 5, page 46

1. Force	6. 6.28×10^{18}	11. Amperes	16. 373 watts
2. Pounds	7. Coulombs	12. 746	17. $\frac{1}{2}$ h.p.
3. Foot pounds	8. Rate	13. Amperes	18. 3
4. Volts	9. Motion	14. 20 ft. lbs.	19. 1.5
5. Joules	10. Watt	15. 30 Joules	20. 50 joules

UNIT 6, page 60

1. 2 amperes	6. 200 volts	11. Greater
2. 150 volts	7. 100 watts	12. Greater
3. No	8. Greater	13. Greater
4. 1150 watts	9. Greater	14. Lesser
5. .15 ampere	10. Greater	15. Greater

16. *a*) 24 ohms; *b*) less; *c*) less; *d*) less
17. *a*) more; *b*) less; *c*) less
18. *b*) (one-half as much)
19. *a*) (twice as much)
20. 2 amperes

UNIT 7, page 80

1. *a*) 12 volts; *b*) 12 volts
2. 4 amperes at all points
3. 16 ohms
4. 1.0 volts across 2 ohms; 1.5 volts across 3 ohms; .5 volts across 1 ohm
   3.0 volts across 6 ohms; 2.0 volts across 4 ohms
5. Not enough information supplied. It cannot be determined.
6. 400 watts
7. They are all the same, series circuits.

UNIT 8, page 91

1. No!   4. Same as source.   7. 16 watts
2. Stop flowing.   5. 2 volts
3. Continue to flow.   6. 5 to 1
8.

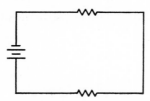

9.

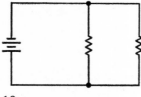

10.

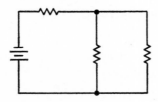

UNIT 9, page 107

1. The current entering a circuit equals the current leaving it.

2. The sum of the voltage drops around a circuit equals the voltage applied across the circuit.

3. 5 amperes   4. 7 amperes   5. 105 volts   6. 6 volts

7. It is impossible.

8.   9.

   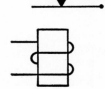

10.

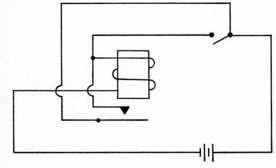

UNIT 10, page 119

1. 1×10^2	10. 1.5×10^4	19. 1×10^3	28. 1,200,000
2. 1×10^4	11. 1.5×10^{-2}	20. 1×10^6	29. 5600
3. 1×10^6	12. 3	21. 1×10^{-3}	30. 7.6
4. 1×10^{-2}	13. 6	22. 1×10^{-6}	31. 6.6
5. 1×10^{-3}	14. -3	23. 2000	32. .0000013
6. 1×10^{-6}	15. 1×10^3	24. 2,000,000	33. .125
7. 1×10^{-12}	16. 1×10^6	25. .010	34. 250
8. 1.5×10^3	17. 1×10^{-3}	26. 10,000	35. 100
9. 1.5×10^2	18. 1×10^{-6}	27. 1000	

UNIT 11, page 143

1. It is a unit of capacitance. A capacitor which can store 1 coulomb under a pressure of 1 volt has a capacitance of 1 farad.

2. .012 coulomb or 1.2×10^{-2}
3. .003 coulomb or 3×10^{-3}
4. 120 mfd.
5. .25 mfd.
6. 8.3 mfd.
7. 2.87 mfd.
8. 2.5 joules
9. 3.125 joules
10. Not enough information given.
11. 60 milliseconds
12. 10 seconds

UNIT 12, page 155
1. Current flow, north
2. Ammeter
3. Voltmeter
4. Multiplier
5. Shunt
6. Series
7. Parallel
8. Ohmmeter
9. Multirange
10. Rectifier
11. Copper oxide
12. Alternating current to direct current.
13. Half
14. Full
15. Multimeter

UNIT 13, page 179
1. North
2. North, south
3. Armature rotation
4. 90°
5. One
6. Direct current
7. Alternating current
8. Armature
9. Rheostat
10. Low
11. Poor
12. Compound
13. Single
14. Two
15. Three
16. Induction
17. High

UNIT 14, page 212

1. 3768
2. 6.28
3. 50 ohms
4. 110 ohms
5. 5 ohms
6. 60 watts
7. *a*
8. Increases
9. Decreases
10. Power factor
11. True
12. False

UNIT 15, page 228

1. 10
2. Capacitive, 30
3. 5
4. 45°
5. 45°
6. 0°
7. 90°
8. 90°
9. Amperage
10. Voltage
11. $E \times I$
12. $E \times I \times P.F.$
13. Resonance
14. Maximum
15. Minimum

UNIT 16, page 240

1. 1000
2. .1 ampere
3. 100
4. 10
5. 10
6. 10
7. Few, air
8. Iron
9. Pure direct current
10. Autotransformer
11. Shock hazard
12. Series

UNIT 17, page 250

1.

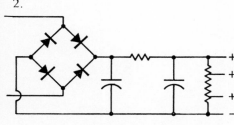

2.

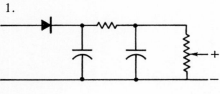

3.

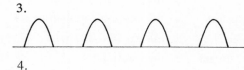

4.

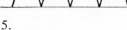

5.

ZERO

ELECTRICAL ABBREVIATIONS

a.c.	alternating current
a, A, amp	ampere
C	capacitance in farads
∿	cycle
I	current, effective flow in amps
d.c.	direct current
E	effective emf in volts
emf	electromotive force, voltage
f	farad; frequency in cycles per second
h, H	henry
h.p.	horsepower, 746 watts
K	kilo, multiplier (1000 or 10^3)
L	inductance in henries
m	milli, .001 part (10^{-3})
ma, mA	milliampere, milliammeter
μ, u	micro, .000,001 part (10^{-6})
μf, uf, mf	microfarad
$\mu\mu$f, mmf	micromicrofarad (*same as* pf *or* picofarad)
MΩ, meg.	megohm, 1,000,000 ohms
Ω	ohm, omega
P	power in watts or joules per second
P.F.	power factor
π	3.1416, pi
R, r	resistance in ohms
rms, R.M.S.	root mean square
T, t	time or period
V	volt, voltage, electromotive force
w	watts, unit of power
X	reactance (X_L or X_C) in ohms
X_L	inductive reactance in ohms
X_C	capacitive reactance in ohms
Z	impedance, or total opposition of an a.c. circuit expressed in ohms

MATHEMATICAL FORMULAS

Resistance Formulas

In Series: $\qquad R_t = R_1 + R_2 \times R_3 \ldots$ etc.

In Parallel: $\qquad R_t = \dfrac{1}{\dfrac{1}{R_1} + \dfrac{1}{R_2} + \dfrac{1}{R_3} + \ldots \text{ etc.}}$

or $\qquad R_t = \dfrac{R_1\,R_2}{R_1 + R_2}$

Capacitance Formulas

In Parallel: $\qquad C_t = C_1 + C_2 + C_3 \ldots$ etc.

In Series: $\qquad C_t = \dfrac{1}{\dfrac{1}{C_1} + \dfrac{1}{C_2} + \dfrac{1}{C_3} + \ldots \text{ etc.}}$

or $\qquad C_t = \dfrac{C_1\,C_2}{C_1 + C_2}$

Resonance Formula

$$f_r = \dfrac{1}{2\,\pi\,\sqrt{L\,C}}$$

Reactance Formulas

Inductive: $\qquad X_L = 2\,\pi\,f\,L$

Capacitive: $\qquad X_C = \dfrac{1}{2\,\pi\,f\,C}$

Impedance Formulas

For Series: $\qquad Z = \sqrt{R^2 + (X_L - X_C)^2}$

For Parallel: $\qquad Z = \dfrac{R\,X_L\,X_C}{\sqrt{X_L^2\,X_C^2 + (R\,X_L - R\,X_C)^2}}$

D.C. Voltage Formulas

$$E = I\,R \qquad\qquad E = \dfrac{P}{I} \qquad\qquad E = \sqrt{P\,R}$$

D.C. Amperage Formulas

$$I = \frac{E}{R} \qquad I = \sqrt{\frac{P}{R}} \qquad I = \frac{P}{E}$$

D.C. Resistance Formulas

$$R = \frac{E}{I} \qquad R = \frac{P}{I^2} \qquad R = \frac{E^2}{P}$$

D.C. Power Formulas

$$P = I^2 R \qquad P = E I \qquad P = \frac{E^2}{R}$$

A.C. Voltage Formulas

$$E = I Z \qquad E = \frac{P}{I \, \text{Cos} \, \theta} \qquad E = \sqrt{\frac{P Z}{\text{Cos} \, \theta}}$$

A.C. Amperage Formulas

$$I = \frac{E}{Z} \qquad I = \sqrt{\frac{P}{Z \, \text{Cos} \, \theta}} \qquad I = \frac{P}{E \, \text{Cos} \, \theta}$$

A.C. Resistance Formulas

$$Z = \frac{E}{I} \qquad Z = \frac{P}{I^2 \, \text{Cos} \, \theta} \qquad Z = \frac{E^2 \, \text{Cos} \, \theta}{P}$$

A.C. Power Formulas

$$P = I^2 Z \, \text{Cos} \, \theta \qquad P = I E \, \text{Cos} \, \theta \qquad P = \frac{E^2 \, \text{Cos} \, \theta}{Z}$$

MATHEMATICAL CONSTANTS AND SYMBOLS

$$\pi = 3.1416$$

$$\sqrt{\pi} = 1.7725$$

$$\frac{1}{\sqrt{\pi}} = 0.5642$$

$$2\pi = 6.2832$$

$\times$ or $\cdot$	Multiplied by.
$\div$	Divided by.
$=$	Equals.
$\neq$	Does not equal.
$+$	Positive, add, and plus.
$-$	Negative, subtract, and minus.
$>$	Is greater than.
$<$	Is less than.
$\angle$	Angle.
$\pm$	Plus or minus.
$\sqrt{}$	Square root.

NATURAL TRIGONOMETRIC FUNCTIONS

Degrees	Sin	Cos	Tan	Cot	
0° 00'	0.0000	1.0000	0.0000	∞	90° 00'
10	.0029	1.0000	.0029	343.77	50
20	.0058	1.0000	.0058	171.89	40
30	.0087	1.0000	.0087	114.59	30
40	.0116	.9999	.0116	85.940	20
50	.0145	.9999	.0145	68.750	10
1° 00'	0.0175	0.9998	0.0175	57.290	89° 00'
10	.0204	.9998	.0204	49.104	50
20	.0233	.9997	.0233	42.964	40
30	.0262	.9997	.0262	38.188	30
40	.0291	.9996	.0291	34.368	20
50	.0320	.9995	.0320	31.242	10
2° 00'	0.0349	0.9994	0.0349	28.636	88° 00'
10	.0378	.9993	.0378	26.432	50
20	.0407	.9992	.0407	24.542	40
30	.0436	.9990	.0437	22.904	30
40	.0465	.9989	.0466	21.470	20
50	.0494	.9988	.0495	20.206	10
3° 00'	0.0523	0.9986	0.0524	19.081	87° 00'
10	.0552	.9985	.0553	18.075	50
20	.0581	.9983	.0582	17.169	40
30	.0610	.9981	.0612	16.350	30
40	.0640	.9980	.0641	15.605	20
50	.0669	.9978	.0670	14.924	10
4° 00'	0.0698	0.9976	0.0699	14.301	86° 00'
10	.0727	.9974	.0729	13.727	50
20	.0756	.9971	.0758	13.197	40
30	.0785	.9969	.0787	12.706	30
40	.0814	.9967	.0816	12.251	20
50	.0843	.9964	.0846	11.826	10
5° 00'	0.0872	0.9962	0.0875	11.430	85° 00'
10	.0901	.9959	.0904	11.059	50
20	.0929	.9957	.0934	10.712	40
30	.0958	.9954	.0963	10.385	30
40	.0987	.9951	.0992	10.078	20
50	.1016	.9948	.1022	9.7882	10
	Cos	Sin	Cot	Tan	Degrees

Degrees	Sin	Cos	Tan	Cot	
6° 00′	0.1045	0.9945	0.1051	9.5144	84° 00′
10	.1074	.9942	.1080	9.2553	50
20	.1103	.9939	.1110	9.0098	40
30	.1132	.9936	.1139	8.7769	30
40	.1161	.9932	.1169	8.5555	20
50	.1190	.9929	.1198	8.3450	10
7° 00′	0.1219	0.9925	0.1228	8.1443	83° 00′
10	.1248	.9922	.1257	7.9530	50
20	.1276	.9918	.1287	7.7704	40
30	.1305	.9914	.1317	7.5958	30
40	.1334	.9911	.1346	7.4287	20
50	.1363	.9907	.1376	7.2687	10
8° 00′	0.1392	0.9903	0.1405	7.1154	82° 00′
10	.1421	.9899	.1435	6.9632	50
20	.1449	.9894	.1465	6.8269	40
30	.1478	.9890	.1495	6.6912	30
40	.1507	.9886	.1524	6.5606	20
50	.1536	.9881	.1554	6.4348	10
9° 00′	0.1564	0.9877	0.1584	6.3138	81° 00′
10	.1593	.9872	.1614	6.1970	50
20	.1622	.9868	.1644	6.0844	40
30	.1650	.9863	.1673	5.9758	30
40	.1679	.9858	.1703	5.8708	20
50	.1708	.9853	.1733	5.7692	10
10° 00′	0.1736	0.9848	0.1763	5.6713	80° 00′
10	.1765	.9843	.1793	5.5764	50
20	.1794	.9838	.1823	5.4845	40
30	.1822	.9833	.1853	5.3955	30
40	.1851	.9827	.1883	5.3093	20
50	.1880	.9822	.1914	5.2257	10
11° 00′	0.1908	0.9816	0.1944	5.1446	79° 00′
10	.1937	.9811	.1974	5.0653	50
20	.1965	.9805	.2004	4.9894	40
30	.1994	.9799	.2035	4.9152	30
40	.2022	.9793	.2065	4.8430	20
50	.2051	.9787	.2095	4.7729	10
12° 00′	0.2079	0.9781	0.2126	4.7046	78° 00′
10	.2108	.9775	.2156	4.6332	50
20	.2136	.9769	.2186	4.5736	40
30	.2164	.9763	.2217	4.5107	30
40	.2193	.9757	.2247	4.4494	20
50	.2221	.9750	.2278	4.3897	10
	Cos	Sin	Cot	Tan	Degrees

Degrees	Sin	Cos	Tan	Cot	
13° 00′	0.2250	0.9744	0.2309	4.3315	77° 00′
10	.2278	.9737	.2339	4.2747	50
20	.2306	.9730	.2370	4.2193	40
30	.2334	.9724	.2401	4.1653	30
40	.2363	.9717	.2432	4.1126	20
50	.2391	.9710	.2462	4.0611	10
14° 00′	0.2419	0.9703	0.2493	4.0108	76° 00′
10	.2447	.9696	.2524	3.9617	50
20	.2476	.9689	.2555	3.9136	40
30	.2504	.9681	.2586	3.8667	30
40	.2532	.9674	.2617	3.8208	20
50	.2560	.9667	.2648	3.7760	10
15° 00′	0.2588	0.9659	0.2679	3.7321	75° 00′
10	.2616	.9652	.2711	3.6891	50
20	.2644	.9644	.2742	3.6470	40
30	.2672	.9636	.2773	3.6059	30
40	.2700	.9628	.2805	3.5656	20
50	.2728	.9621	.2836	3.5261	10
16° 00′	0.2756	0.9613	0.2867	3.4874	74° 00′
10	.2784	.9605	.2899	3.4495	50
20	.2812	.9596	.2931	3.4124	40
30	.2840	.9588	.2962	3.3759	30
40	.2868	.9580	.2994	3.3402	20
50	.2896	.9572	.3026	3.3052	10
17° 00′	0.2924	0.9563	0.3057	3.2709	73° 00′
10	.2952	.9555	.3089	3.2371	50
20	.2979	.9546	.3121	3.2041	40
30	.3007	.9537	.3153	3.1716	30
40	.3035	.9528	.3185	3.1397	20
50	.3062	.9520	.3217	3.1084	10
18° 00′	0.3090	0.9511	0.3249	3.0777	72° 00′
10	.3118	.9502	.3281	3.0475	50
20	.3145	.9492	.3314	3.0178	40
30	.3173	.9483	.3346	2.9887	30
40	.3201	.9474	.3378	2.9600	20
50	.3228	.9465	.3411	2.9319	10
19° 00′	0.3256	0.9455	0.3443	2.9042	71° 00′
10	.3283	.9446	.3476	2.8770	50
20	.3311	.9436	.3508	2.8502	40
30	.3338	.9426	.3541	2.8239	30
40	.3365	.9417	.3574	2.7980	20
50	.3393	.9407	.3607	2.7725	10
	Cos	Sin	Cot	Tan	Degrees

Degrees	Sin	Cos	Tan	Cot	
20° 00'	0.3420	0.9397	0.3640	2.7475	70° 00'
10	.3448	.9387	.3673	2.7228	50
20	.3475	.9377	.3706	2.6985	40
30	.3502	.9367	.3739	2.6746	30
40	.3529	.9356	.3772	2.6511	20
50	.3557	.9346	.3805	2.6279	10
21° 00'	0.3584	0.9336	0.3839	2.6051	69° 00'
10	.3611	.9325	.3872	2.5826	50
20	.3638	.9315	.3906	2.5605	40
30	.3665	.9304	.3939	2.5386	30
40	.3692	.9293	.3973	2.5172	20
50	.3719	.9283	.4006	2.4960	10
22° 00'	0.3746	0.9272	0.4040	2.4751	68° 00'
10	.3773	.9261	.4074	2.4545	50
20	.3800	.9250	.4108	2.4342	40
30	.3827	.9239	.4142	2.4142	30
40	.3854	.9228	.4176	2.3945	20
50	.3881	.9216	.4210	2.3750	10
23° 00'	0.3907	0.9205	0.4245	2.3559	67° 00'
10	.3934	.9194	.4279	2.3369	50
20	.3961	.9182	.4314	2.3183	40
30	.3987	.9171	.4348	2.2998	30
40	.4014	.9159	.4383	2.2817	20
50	.4041	.9147	.4417	2.2637	10
24° 00'	0.4067	0.9135	0.4452	2.2460	66° 00'
10	.4094	.9124	.4487	2.2286	50
20	.4120	.9112	.4522	2.2113	40
30	.4147	.9100	.4557	2.1943	30
40	.4173	.9088	.4592	2.1775	20
50	.4200	.9075	.4628	2.1609	10
25° 00'	0.4226	0.9063	0.4663	2.1445	65° 00'
10	.4253	.9051	.4699	2.1283	50
20	.4279	.9038	.4734	2.1123	40
30	.4305	.9026	.4770	2.0965	30
40	.4331	.9013	.4806	2.0809	20
50	.4358	.9001	.4841	2.0655	10
26° 00'	0.4384	0.8988	0.4877	2.0503	64° 00'
10	.4410	.8975	.4913	2.0353	50
20	.4436	.8962	.4950	2.0204	40
30	.4462	.8949	.4986	2.0057	30
40	.4488	.8936	.5022	1.9912	20
50	.4514	.8923	.5059	1.9768	10
	Cos	Sin	Cot	Tan	Degrees

Degrees	Sin	Cos	Tan	Cot	
27° 00′	0.4540	0.8910	0.5095	1.9626	63° 00′
10	.4566	.8897	.5132	1.9486	50
20	.4592	.8884	.5169	1.9347	40
30	.4617	.8870	.5206	1.9210	30
40	.4643	.8857	.5243	1.9074	20
50	.4669	.8843	.5280	1.8940	10
28° 00′	0.4695	0.8829	0.5317	1.8807	62° 00′
10	.4720	.8816	.5354	1.8676	50
20	.4746	.8802	.5392	1.8546	40
30	.4772	.8788	.5430	1.8418	30
40	.4797	.8774	.5467	1.8291	20
50	.4823	.8760	.5505	1.8165	10
29° 00′	0.4848	0.8746	0.5543	1.8040	61° 00′
10	.4874	.8732	.5581	1.7917	50
20	.4899	.8718	.5619	1.7796	40
30	.4924	.8704	.5658	1.7675	30
40	.4950	.8689	.5696	1.7556	20
50	.4975	.8675	.5735	1.7437	10
30° 00′	0.5000	0.8660	0.5774	1.7321	60° 00′
10	.5025	.8646	.5812	1.7205	50
20	.5050	.8631	.5851	1.7090	40
30	.5075	.8616	.5890	1.6977	30
40	.5100	.8601	.5930	1.6864	20
50	.5125	.8587	.5969	1.6753	10
31° 00′	0.5150	0.8572	0.6009	1.6643	59° 00′
10	.5175	.8557	.6048	1.6534	50
20	.5200	.8542	.6088	1.6426	40
30	.5225	.8526	.6128	1.6319	30
40	.5250	.8511	.6168	1.6212	20
50	.5275	.8496	.6208	1.6107	10
32° 00′	0.5299	0.8480	0.6249	1.6003	58° 00′
10	.5324	.8465	.6289	1.5900	50
20	.5348	.8450	.6330	1.5798	40
30	.5373	.8434	.6371	1.5697	30
40	.5398	.8418	.6412	1.5597	20
50	.5422	.8403	.6453	1.5497	10
33° 00′	0.5446	0.8387	0.6494	1.5399	57° 00′
10	.5471	.8371	.6536	1.5301	50
20	.5495	.8355	.6577	1.5204	40
30	.5519	.8339	.6619	1.5108	30
40	.5544	.8323	.6661	1.5013	20
50	.5568	.8307	.6703	1.4919	10
	Cos	Sin	Cot	Tan	Degrees

Degrees	Sin	Cos	Tan	Cot	
34° 00′	0.5592	0.8290	0.6745	1.4826	56° 00′
10	.5616	.8274	.6787	1.4733	50
20	.5640	.8285	.6830	1.4641	40
30	.5664	.8241	.6873	1.4550	30
40	.5688	.8225	.6916	1.4460	20
50	.5712	.8208	.6959	1.4370	10
35° 00′	0.5736	0.8192	0.7002	1.4281	55° 00′
10	.5760	.8175	.7046	1.4193	50
20	.5783	.8158	.7089	1.4106	40
30	.5807	.8141	.7133	1.4019	30
40	.5831	.8124	.7177	1.3934	20
50	.5854	.8107	.7221	1.3848	10
36° 00′	0.5878	0.8090	0.7265	1.3764	54° 00′
10	.5901	.8073	.7310	1.3680	50
20	.5925	.8056	.7355	1.3597	40
30	.5948	.8039	.7400	1.3514	30
40	.5972	.8021	.7445	1.3432	20
50	.5995	.8004	.7490	1.3351	10
37° 00′	0.6018	0.7986	0.7536	1.3270	53° 00′
10	.6041	.7969	.7581	1.3190	50
20	.6065	.7951	.7627	1.3111	40
30	.6088	.7934	.7673	1.3032	30
40	.6111	.7916	.7720	1.2954	20
50	.6134	.7898	.7766	1.2876	10
38° 00′	0.6157	0.7880	0.7813	1.2799	52° 00′
10	.6180	.7862	.7860	1.2723	50
20	.6202	.7844	.7907	1.2647	40
30	.6225	.7826	.7954	1.2572	30
40	.6248	.7808	.8002	1.2497	20
50	.6271	.7790	.8050	1.2423	10
39° 00′	0.6293	0.7771	0.8098	1.2349	51° 00′
10	.6316	.7753	.8146	1.2276	50
20	.6338	.7735	.8195	1.2203	40
30	.6361	.7716	.8243	1.2131	30
40	.6383	.7698	.8292	1.2059	20
50	.6406	.7679	.8342	1.1988	10
40° 00′	0.6428	0.7660	0.8391	1.1918	50° 00′
10	.6450	.7642	.8441	1.1847	50
20	.6472	.7623	.8491	1.1778	40
30	.6494	.7604	.8541	1.1708	30
40	.6517	.7585	.8591	1.1640	20
50	.6539	.7566	.8642	1.1571	10
	Cos	Sin	Cot	Tan	Degrees

Degrees	Sin	Cos	Tan	Cot	
41° 00'	0.6561	0.7547	0.8693	1.1504	49° 00'
10	.6583	.7528	.8744	1.1436	50
20	.6604	.7509	.8796	1.1369	40
30	.6626	.7490	.8847	1.1303	30
40	.6648	.7470	.8899	1.1237	20
50	.6670	.7451	.8952	1.1171	10
42° 00'	0.6691	0.7431	0.9004	1.1106	48° 00'
10	.6713	.7412	.9057	1.1041	50
20	.6734	.7392	.9110	1.0977	40
30	.6756	.7373	.9163	1.0913	30
40	.6777	.7353	.9217	1.0850	20
50	.6799	.7333	.9271	1.0786	10
43° 00'	0.6820	0.7314	0.9325	1.0724	47° 00'
10	.6841	.7294	.9380	1.0661	50
20	.6862	.7274	.9435	1.0599	40
30	.6884	.7254	.9490	1.0538	30
40	.6905	.7234	.9545	1.0477	20
50	.6926	.7214	.9601	1.0416	10
44° 00'	0.6947	0.7193	0.9657	1.0355	46° 00'
10	.6967	.7173	.9713	1.0295	50
20	.6988	.7163	.9770	1.0235	40
30	.7009	.7133	.9827	1.0176	30
40	.7030	.7112	.9884	1.0117	20
50	.7050	.7092	.9942	1.0058	10
45° 00'	0.7071	0.7071	1.0000	1.0000	45° 00'
	Cos	Sin	Cot	Tan	Degrees

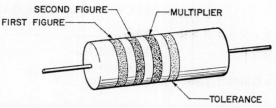

RESISTOR COLOR CODE

Color	1st Digit	2nd Digit	Multiplier	Tolerance
Black	0	0	1	. . .
Brown	1	1	10	. . .
Red	2	2	100	. . .
Orange	3	3	1,000	. . .
Yellow	4	4	10,000	. . .
Green	5	5	100,000	. . .
Blue	6	6	1,000,000	. . .
Violet	7	7	10,000,000	. . .
Gray	8	8	100,000,000	. . .
White	9	9	. . .	. . .
Gold	. . .	. . .	0.1	± 5%
Silver	. . .	. . .	0.01*	± 10%
No Color	. . .	. . .	. . .	± 20%

* Retma only.

MICA CAPACITOR COLOR CODE
Military Standard MIL-C-5A

Color	Digits of Capacitance ($\mu\mu$f.)		Multiplier	Tolerance (%)	Characteristic, See table below
Black	0	0	1	± 20	. . .
Brown	1	1	10	. . .	B
Red	2	2	100	± 2	C
Orange	3	3	1,000	. . .	D
Yellow	4	4	. . .	. . .	E
Green	5	5	. . .	. . .	F
Blue	6	6	. . .	. . .	. . .
Violet	7	7	. . .	. . .	. . .
Gray	8	8	. . .	. . .	. . .
White	9	9	. . .	. . .	. . .
Gold	. . .	. . .	0.1	± 5	. . .
Silver	. . .	. . .	0.01	± 10	. . .

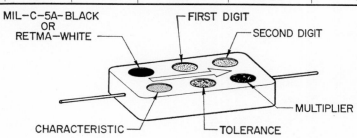

271

DESCRIPTION OF CHARACTERISTIC

Characteristic	Temperature Coefficient (parts per million per °C)	Maximum Capacitance Drift	Minimum Insulation Resistance (megohms)
B	Not specified	Not specified	7500
C	± 200	± 0.5%	7500
D	± 100	± 0.3%	7500
E	+100 − 20	± (0.1% + 0.1 $\mu\mu$f.)	7500
F	+ 70	± (0.05% + 0.1 $\mu\mu$f.)	7500

VOLTAGE RATING

(Indicated by dimensions rather than color coding)

Maximum Inches			Style CM	Capacitance ($\mu\mu$f.)	Rating (v d-c)
Long	Wide	Thick			
$\frac{35}{64}$	$\frac{5}{16}$	$\frac{7}{32}$	15	5–510	300
$\frac{51}{64}$	$\frac{15}{32}$	$\frac{7}{32}$	20	5–510 560–1000	500 300
$1\frac{7}{64}$	$\frac{15}{32}$	$\frac{7}{32}$	25	51–1000	500
$\frac{53}{64}$	$\frac{53}{64}$	$\frac{9}{32}$	30	560–3300	500
$\frac{53}{64}$	$\frac{53}{64}$	$\frac{11}{32}$	35	3600–6200 6800–10,000	500 300
$1\frac{1}{32}$	$\frac{41}{64}$	$\frac{11}{32}$	40	3300–8200 9100–10,000	500 300

INDEX